KING OF SINNERS

King *of* Sinners

EDDIE DOHERTY

57977

THE BRUCE PUBLISHING COMPANY • MILWAUKEE

Nihil obstat:
>   Rev. M. J. Hass
>   *Censor librorum*

Imprimatur:
>   ✠ William Joseph Smith
>   *Bishop of Pembroke*
>   *Ontario, Canada*
>   December 3rd, 1963

Library of Congress Catalog Card Number: 63–22040

© 1964 The Bruce Publishing Company
MADE IN THE UNITED STATES OF AMERICA

TO THE HOLY FAMILY

Joseph, Mary, and Jesus,
I give You my heart and my soul;
and the fruits of all my years.

KING OF SINNERS

Introit

Once upon a time, in a kingdom by the sea, the God who made all nations and all things came to earth as a newborn child. He came to weld all nations into one fine kingdom, and to teach all men that they are brothers. His name was Jesus. He lived and died among us.

The world was smaller then; and there was peace, of a sort, for the sword that ruled it forced the poor to behave, work hard, produce, pay taxes, and submit to Caesar's will. The story of Jesus changed the minds of men and freed the people. But the world grew, and evil grew with it. And wars came. And men changed the story to suit themselves — some even putting the tyrant's sword into the hand of the Good Shepherd!

In spite of all this the story lived. Each generation has loved it, taught it, and embroidered it with details born of reverence and imagination; for, since it is everybody's story, anybody has a right to tell it his own way — so long as he does not contradict the Gospels.

So let us now try to retell this story, making up, as we go along, the incidents we need to link together the facts related by Matthew, Mark, Luke, and John. Let us make them up boldly; as though we saw them happen. Let us not be timid in our guesses, where we are permitted to guess. Let us speak of

Mary and Joseph as though they were never strangers to us.
Let us picture Jesus as our hearts see him — in those stories
not related by the evangelists. And let us picture Lucifer as
imagination sees him. We must see him mostly as a spirit, the
spirit of evil. He is the villain of our story. He must not be
ignored. There are people who do not believe he exists; but the
Bible says he does. Saints and mystics have encountered him,
and have tried to give us some description of him. Sometimes
he assumes a body. Sometimes he takes possession of a body.
He is one of the most powerful of the angels, yet one of the
most easily humiliated and frightened. He is also easily enraged;
and he is a frightful enemy. He is a creature of extremes. He
is intelligent. He is a fool. He is strong. He is weak. He is a
shifty, inconsistent, sleazy character. Let us treat him as such.

In telling the story, let us not be too troubled about the order
in which we present the incidents in the life of Jesus. The
evangelists were not concerned about any "chronology." They
were interested in what Jesus did and said, not when he did or
said it. There is no exact time pattern to follow. We can arrange
the events the way we think we should. There is no reason,
anyway, why we should follow any certain pattern, since we are
guessing at so much of our story.

Let us not pretend that what we make up is the truth, the
whole truth, and nothing but the truth. Let us admit we merely
believe we are telling the story as it might have happened, that
we have no divine inspiration such as animated the evangelists,
and that we are not at all infallible.

There are many versions of the Bible. When we quote from it,
let us use the Douay-Challoner version, or the Confraternity
edition, whichever seems clearer. And let us, with God's help,
do the best we can. Then, perhaps, more readers will love and
adore the Lord Jesus.

CHAPTER I

In the fullness of time almighty God summoned an angel and sent him to earth on the most stupendous errand in eternity or time.

"You will go to Nazareth, in Galilee," he said, "to a virgin named Mary. You will give her my love. And you will ask her to be the mother of my Son."

One who knows nothing of heaven might suspect there was unusual excitement when the news was learned. The Lord's long courtship of men was nearing a glorious climax. The sinners he had loved — and put up with — for so many thousands of years might soon be coming up to share his bliss. There were millions and millions and millions of them! And they kept growing in numbers all the time, unlike the angels. There was no counting them! If the courts of heaven are anything like the royal courts of earth, the news was soon spreading through all the kingdom; and all the holy spirits were talking:

"The Son of God is going to become Man . . . born of a woman. A woman! How God must love her! . . . We are going to have a queen. . . . Why does the Most High love sinners so? . . . And we are to have people up here. . . . After all these centuries!"

If we make God and the angels speak our language it is be-

cause Scripture gave us the example, and because we cannot
know what language, if any, they really speak. If we put foolish
thoughts in God's mouth, the foolishness is ours. But we do it
with love and reverence.

"Be gentle with her, Gabriel," God said. "She is most dear
to me. Woo her for me. A woman must be wooed and won.
Give her your love and mine, for she will be your queen. Give
her your loyalty as well. And hail her as 'full of grace'!"

Mary was fourteen then, or perhaps a little older. Legend
has it that she was presented in the Temple, in Jerusalem, when
she was three years old, and that she remained there eleven
years, perfecting herself in a hundred different ways. She had
been sent home to Nazareth that she might be married. Girls
of her age were always given in marriage. It was the custom.
It was the law. There was nothing they could do about it. They
were not consulted. Marriages were arranged that children might
be born, for one of these might be the Messiah, the Christ, the
Prophet, the Redeemer promised by God so many many years
before.

Some writers say Mary lived with her parents, Joachim and
Ann, in a comfortable house in Nazareth. Some say she lived
in a hut, or a cave, and that she lived alone, her parents having
died — or that she lived with a cousin or an aunt or some other
relative. Some say her marriage to Joseph was arranged by
priests in Jerusalem; others that relatives made all the arrangements. We know it was arranged by God. And we know it was
a "love match."

The romance of Mary and Joseph is one of the great dramas
directed by Infinite Love. Yet it has never been written. The
men of old slighted or distorted it, in a clumsy attempt to protect
Mary's reputation for angelic purity — a reputation that needed
no protection. Men of other ages have ignored the romance.

Most of these men pictured Joseph as so old he could not

possibly think of loving any girl — even so wonderful a girl as
Mary. They wrinkled his hands and face. They bleared his eyes.
They gave him a white thin beard, long enough to strangle a
donkey; and they would have made him deaf, dumb, blind,
senile, and paralyzed if they could; so that nobody would think
he was any sort of threat to Mary's chastity.

But they dared not go too far in their pious frauds, for they
needed the man to lead the way to Bethlehem, and to take the
Child and his mother to the safety of Egypt, to make a living
for them there, and to bring them back. One writer made Joseph
90 years old when he married the virgin. But he let him live to
be 128!

Joseph must have been a nuisance to these writers. He was
the essential suitor and husband, the necessary foster father, the
much needed protector and provider. He could not be ignored.
The storytellers had nothing against Joseph. They knew he was
a saint. But they couldn't stand the idea of his making love to
Mary. So they acted accordingly; they made a legend of him.
In doing so they invented one of the oddest miracles in the
history of the written word.

They were inspired by the story of Aaron's rod, and by a
misinterpretation of a prophecy of Isaias: "And there shall come
forth a rod out of the root of Jesse, and a flower shall rise up
out of his root. And the spirit of the Lord shall rest upon him."

When the Most High had wanted to let the children of Israel
know that the sons of Levi were to be his priests, he bade Aaron
collect twelve rods, one from each of the tribes, and "lay them
up in the tabernacle of the covenant." Aaron was to place his
own rod there too, which was to represent the house of Levi.
His rod budded overnight, bore almond blossoms, and even full-
grown almonds. The Lord had chosen!

Thus, it was easy to invent an army of handsome young men,
all sons of the house of David, all rich, all ardent lovers of Mary.

The writers were generous. They gave the virgin 3000 of these suitors. Joseph was invited to join, since he was also of the house of David and the "root of Jesse." But Joseph, they explained, wanted only to be left alone. He could not be coaxed into the competition until he learned the girl had property which must stay in the house of David. Her house would belong to the man she married. This was the bait that hooked poor doddering Joseph!

The priests made each of the 3001 candidates put his walking stick on the altar — then waited for heaven to act. In 3000 cases nothing happened. Nothing at all. But with Stick No. 3001 — what an amazing difference!

That dead and dried-up piece of wood suddenly sprouted a gorgeous fresh white lily. One could smell it all over the city of Jerusalem. And then, as if that weren't sign enough of heaven's choice, the writers dropped a white dove out of the murky clouds of their imagination, and let it hover above the flower like a humming bird!

Whose cane was it? Poor old slandered Joseph's! Furthermore, some of his statues still carry that blooming stick today!

If it had occurred to those writers that Joseph had the blood of mystics, prophets, poets, woman-crazy kings, and other saintly and sinful sires in his veins, they would have accused themselves of blasphemy, and lived the rest of their lives in sackcloth and ashes. Yet, modern students of the Bible assure us Joseph was young when he was betrothed to Mary. He may have been anywhere between eighteen and twenty-five. He was strong, a skillful workman, and well able to support a wife and family. He was certainly not in the least reluctant to marry the loveliest woman in the world, and her property meant nothing to him.

God selected His Son's mother and His foster father with infinite wisdom. God wants a normal human love in every home on earth, love between father and mother, love between parents and children. He would not want Jesus brought up in a loveless household; for he was to live and die for love. He selected Mary not only because she was without any taint of sin, but also because she was so filled with love. And he selected Joseph because of the riches in his great warm heart.

It is quite possible there were other young men in Nazareth who had wanted to marry the beautiful virgin. But not 3000. There were not 3000 men, young or old, in the village.

Mary was the most beautiful creature God had ever made. She was as perfect as Infinite Perfection could make her. She was made in heaven. She had lived in heaven in the mind, in the very essence of the Most High, throughout eternity. She was made to be a heaven on earth. She was filled with holiness and wisdom. She was filled with grace. She was filled with the glory of God; and she drew all men to God.

Her beauty was of the quiet kind. She attracted men, naturally; but talked to them about God when they wanted to talk to her about themselves. She could not help making a man feel like the clumsiest of mortals.

Joseph's heart leaped to her when he saw her; and he demanded her, instantly, in marriage. He too saw she had a quiet beauty. But he learned that, in some moods, her beauty shone with such dazzling luster as to stun and awe and silence those around her. And he loved the way she talked of God.

They were betrothed as soon as possible; and, to Joseph's astonishment and delight, the maiden made not a single protest. Half of Nazareth celebrated the affair — and wondered more about Joseph than about the woman he had chosen.

A betrothal then was, to all intents and purposes, a valid marriage. The girl was considered a wife. If the man died before marriage, she would be his legal widow, with all a widow's rights. She could be divorced. And she could be stoned to death if she sinned against her husband. Girls were usually betrothed young and married later — when the home was ready. Joseph began to prepare a proper home; yet day and night he left his workshop and whatever task had occupied him, to stroll by Mary's house. He passed it without seeming to glance at it, though he had gone out of his way to pass it.

He didn't linger about the place, though he wanted to do so. Men would laugh if they knew he thought that poor grotto was the holiest and loveliest spot on earth. He hurried away always. But he would soon be back again, to pass by as swiftly as before.

When he saw the girl herself, walking to the well, perhaps, or coming home from it, his heart seemed to stop beating. Tears stung his eyes, for he was one of those who cannot help shedding tears for beauty. And whatever tool he was handling got away from him. Then his heart began to hammer against his ribs. His chest swelled. His eyes glowed. Color came into his face. He was beautiful. Yet he was unable to walk a step toward her until she came quite close; for he kept thinking, "God could not possibly have given me such a woman; I am living in a dream; if I wake up I shall die; how can I bear the beauty of her?"

Thousands of painters have pictured Mary on her way to the well, a slender barefooted girl with a great pitcher balanced gracefully on her head. The well — where today the water still bubbles up with song and laughter — was only a ten-minute walk, and Mary always passed Joseph's shop on the way. Sometimes she stopped and poured water into his cup and spent a few minutes talking to him.

She talked mostly, it seemed to him, in the language of the God-gifted men of Scripture; and he learned to talk to her — to their mutual delight — as the prophets talked to God.

Sometimes he was David: "O Lord, thou hast crowned us, as with a shield of thy good will."

Sometimes he was David's son: "Arise, make haste, my love, my dove, my beautiful one, and come."

Or he was Jacob: "And Jacob being in love with her said; I will serve thee seven years for Rachel, thy younger daughter . . . seven years . . . and they seemed but a few days because of the greatness of his love."

And sometimes he was himself. "Jacob worked seven years for Rachel, and thought it but a few days. I would work all my life for you — just to be near you; just to see you; just to listen to you talk; just to inhale the perfume of your breath."

He dreamed of her night and day, even while he worked. He worked skillfully and swiftly. He made things for many customers. He made things for the home he was getting ready. Tables for lamps; tables for food; shelves, dozens of shelves. A couch on which Mary might rest at night, after she had prayed to God with all the adoring stars. A cradle. It would be the finest cradle in all Israel. And he could carve bunches of grapes on it, some day, like those on the golden door of the Temple. A cluster of grapes for every little boy and every little girl. And he wished they might all look like their mother. He would paint those grapes. One bunch would be a royal purple, one a shiny black, one an inviting green, one a tempting golden yellow. Grapes, thank God, had many colors!

One spring morning when Joseph — as well as all the rest of the world — was excited about the first wild flowers of the year, Mary rested her pitcher on his workbench; and while he held out his cup to her, he looked deeply into her eyes.

Never before had he felt such heavenly elation. It was as though he had been lifted high enough above the earth to peer directly at the very throne of God. And he saw what the Angel Gabriel was to see!

He raised the cup mechanically to his lips, not knowing that he did so. His senses were lost in the heaven of Mary's eyes.

Her voice awakened him. "And now you know why the other men in Nazareth abandoned me."

Joseph sat on a low stool. He sat to keep himself from crashing to the floor. He had fallen from a tremendous height, it seemed to him. And, though he was unhurt, he realized that something terrible had happened. He was stunned at the disaster. But what sort of disaster was it?

He looked up at Mary, and he knew.

He had lost her!

He wondered, idly, if Jacob had felt this way when he learned that his wife was not Rachel but her cross-eyed sister, Leah. Did he too wish he were dead, and beyond all misery of soul and body? No. Not Jacob. Jacob had only to work another seven years, and he would marry Rachel.

But Mary was lost forever!

He thought of the cradle into which he had put so much labor and love and skill, in which he had rocked so many lovely dreams. Poor silly dreams! The cradle mocked him. It would remain forever empty. An empty cradle for an empty life.

"Aye," he said to her. "Now I know. You are my betrothed, and you will marry me. But you will never be my wife. Nor any man's. You belong to God. You belong exclusively to God. It was good of you to let me see that."

He stood up then, encouraged by something new in her. And he was ashamed of the bitterness and the self-pity that had swept through his veins like a corroding acid. He sensed a strange new grace within him; an odd and growing feeling of great peace.

If a king's daughter loves an ordinary man enough to marry him she has only to say to her father, "Make him a prince," and the man will be a prince, no matter what he was before. And if she is the almoner of her father's graces, and can scatter his riches where she will, she can make a millionaire of a pauper.

Joseph rose, ennobled, and enriched with grace, through the will of God's own princess. He was clothed in the splendor that befitted his new rank, his immense new dignity. Thus he could offer himself sincerely and simply to the Lord.

"My sister, my spouse is a garden enclosed," he said. "A fountain sealed up. As the lily among the thorns, so is my love among the daughters. Behold thou art fair, O my love. There is no stain in thee. Thine eyes are dove's eyes. Thy lips are as a scarlet lace, and thy speech sweet. Indeed I know why the other men in Nazareth abandoned you. But I will not abandon you, my love, my dove, my holy one of Galilee. I will be the caretaker of the garden. I will be the guardian of the fountain. You shall remain untouched, inviolate, immaculate, my Mary!"

She took the cup from him and poured the water over his uplifted fingers and down his wrists, in the manner of a Jewish wife purifying her husband's hands before he sits down to his food. He raised his hands and thrust them toward her, water dripping from his wrists, as though to offer — in purity — all his protection, all his strength, and all his many skills.

"No one must pity me," he said, "especially not I myself. For I have had much joy of you. Your breath upon my cheek! The touch of your hands on mine! Once I felt the pulse beating in your wrist, and its melody haunted me for weeks. I walked, as in a dream, to the rhythm of your heartbeats, thinking 'Mary, Mary, Mary!' The feel of your hair blown against my forehead by a blessed wind! A look in your eyes! A tone in your voice! The way you call me 'Prince Joseph.' I am a prince in Israel, since I am of David's line. But nobody else ever called me a prince, nor pronounced my name as though it were sacred music.

"All these are little things; but their fragrance will not die. Aye, I have had more joy of you than King Solomon had from his thousand painted wives. And life has just begun for us — a life of little things; but little things blessed by God!

"The Most High gave you to me only that I might keep you for him. So be it. So be it. Amen. His will is mine. I thank him for his mercy and his love, and for his wondrous trust in me.

"And as a token of my acceptance of that divine trust, I promise, here and now, that I too shall live and die a virgin."

Mary took his hands in hers, and pressed them lightly.

"You have written and sung a song that has lived in my heart since I was a child," she said. "It had no words, yet it was a song of beauty. And it was a song of love. God made me a normal woman, like all the rest of us, with a natural desire for a husband and a child. Yet always, it seems, I knew he wanted me to be a virgin as well as a wife. I did not understand. But always I dreamed of the man who would marry me; and always my heart sang of him to God. I suppose all girls dream of the sort of man they hope to capture. I asked for a prince of purity, one with a heart of fire. I asked for a hero who would love God enough to marry a virgin, and let her stay a virgin for the sake of God. I asked for the man he loved best in all the earth. I asked for you, when I first saw you. I knew you when I saw you, my Prince Joseph. And that was long before you noticed me."

Again Joseph looked deeply into Mary's eyes. This time he did not feel like an intruder.

"Now we are doubly bound," he said. "We are bound by our betrothal vows, and by our vows of chastity. We are more truly one than we were when you came to the well."

"Indeed we are," Mary answered. "For chastity burns away the barriers of flesh, and sets the lovers free to love." She took up her pitcher and raised it to her head.

"And one who has shed his own will," she said, "and clothed himself in the holy will of God has arrayed himself for a royal wedding. You are a prince in Israel, my Joseph. You will be a prince in heaven. And no other prince shall be preferred above you."

CHAPTER II

Mary was alone when the Angel Gabriel came. She was standing just inside the door of her home — a cave made into a house with the skillful use of stones about the entrance and a flat roof of boards covered with rushes and palms. She was looking up at the slender moon and a spatter of pale gold stars. She was thanking God that there was so great and good a man as Joseph, and that soon he would be her husband. She had seen him come home a little while before, leading his donkey. It was large for a donkey, but it looked absurdly small beside its master.

Joseph, as a carpenter in Galilee in that time, got his timber where he found it. He chopped it down, ripped it into boards, and carried it home on his shoulders and on his donkey. He also brought home all the branches he and the beast could carry. Some of these could be used in making furniture. The rest could serve to cook a meal or take the chill off the rocky walls. Joseph also lived in a grotto. He had his workshop there, and a stable for the ass.

The room was dark. But in one of the inner rooms a gay flame danced in a lamp half filled with oil. The lamp rested on a stand that had been made by Joseph.

Abruptly the door closed, shutting out the moon and the stars, shutting out Joseph's grotto, shutting out the world. The room was filled with the radiance of heaven, and Mary saw the angel.

Gabriel looked at the girl in the same moment, and prostrated himself before her, for he beheld the choicest work of God.

There were other angels with him. A mighty king, sending an ambassador to court a princess anywhere on earth, usually sent a great and glittering retinue with him. The King of kings, wooing the loveliest of royal princesses, might have sent the whole court of heaven to accompany his envoy. The other angels, millions of flashes of bright light, also bowed low before the queen-elect of heaven.

It was a great moment in heaven and on earth, a terrible moment in hell. How many other moments have there been, in the long and embarrassing history of mankind, when heaven, hell, and earth must wait for a woman's word?

"Hail full of grace," the messenger of God said softly. "The Lord is with thee. Blessed art thou among women."

The host that was with him sang of peace on earth — as though they were rehearsing it. They would sing it again, so that all the world could hear it, on a night much later in the year.

Mary was startled, but not excited. She received the holy delegation with the poise and the dignity and the graciousness of an earthly queen. She acted as one accustomed to welcoming angels, receiving messages from them, and giving them notes to carry back to the Throne.

She waited for Gabriel to proceed. He was more awed and elated by what he saw than Joseph had been. He had peered deeper into her soul.

It was the will of the Most High, he said, that she become the mother of his Son. She was to call the Child Jesus. He would be a king. God would give him the throne of David. He would reign in the house of Jacob. And his kingdom would endure forever.

Mary listened, and was silent. She knew that the Child would be a king indeed. He would be the Messiah, the Savior, the Redeemer of mankind; but he would not rule over any earthly kingdom.

The singing angels hushed. The Son of God was waiting to come into his kingdom — a kingdom of sinners though it be.

Centuries of sinners penned in Limbo trembled as they waited, listening with the angels. If Gabriel trembled too, it should surprise nobody. Many a proud and powerful man has been frightened, kneeling before a maiden making up her mind.

Suppose she said "no" to God . . .

There were Adam and Eve who had, foolishly, sought to make themselves like unto God. The Almighty might have punished them as he punished the rebellious angels. He might have destroyed the world too. But he had shown mercy, because he had remembered Mary, this girl standing silent now before the shaking Gabriel. Mary and the Seed that she would bear. He had condemned the sinners to toil and tears and hunger and sickness and pain and death; but he had promised them a Redeemer who would turn the kingdom of sinners into a realm of saints, who would banish death, abolish pain, and wipe away all tears. He had remembered Mary when he punished the serpent, the tempter. There would be warfare between that evil thing and the woman, he had said; and between its seed and the seed of the woman. It must lie in wait for her heel.

Now this same God, who had punished man for trying to be God, was asking a daughter of sinful Eve to let him become a Man! And she just stood there and held her little tongue!

The angels could remember another time when God was furious because of the sins of men; when he had determined to drown the world and kill all the life within it. But again he had been softened by the thought of this child-woman, Mary, and the plans he had made for her.

He bade his servant Noe to build an ark so he might save himself and his family from the flood to come, and that he might preserve certain specimens of life. He sent a killing rain upon the earth. The waters rose until they drowned the highest mountain peaks. But the ark, the symbol of Mary, lived — and all the creatures in it.

Earth had been given another chance to love its Maker; but it was as evil now as it had been in the days of Noe. And the creature God had destined to be an ark, a refuge of sinners, might thwart him with a word! If so, why should he not destroy the world?

What the angels did not know was that Mary was too surcharged with emotion to say anything at all. It was all she could do to breathe. She was a girl like others girls in Nazareth. She cooked. She sewed. She kept her house clean. She carried water from the well. She made preparations for her approaching wedding. She made plans for a life with her beloved Joseph. And suddenly, when she was least prepared for such a thing, heaven swooped down to her littleness, as to no other girl, and asked her to become the bride and queen of God, and the mother of his Son!

She realized, to her intense amazement, that this was what she had always wanted to be, without knowing that she wanted it. She had always wanted to have a child. She had always wondered what it would be like to be the mother of the Messiah. What joy such a woman would know! And what atrocious suffering! She realized too that God had been steadily training her for this tremendous task, this duty, this unheard-of honor, this impossible virgin-maternity, this glorious and tragic role. Divine Love had not kept her in ignorance of the frightful death that awaited the Messiah; nor had he hidden the swords that would so often and so cruelly pierce his mother's heart.

She thought of Joseph. She was a virgin and had sworn to remain a virgin, even as Joseph's wife. How then was she to bear a child to God? Not through her love for Joseph. That love must remain immaculate.

When she could talk she asked the question calmly; "How shall this happen, since I do not know man?"

Gabriel explained it simply. The Holy Ghost would come down upon her, and the power of the Most High would over-shadow her. She would be a mother, yet remain a virgin.

"Nothing is impossible to God," the angel assured her. As if to prove his point, he told her that God had heard the prayers of her cousin Elizabeth, a barren old woman who had always wanted a child. She would become the mother of a son.

Mary knew that nothing was impossible to God. He had once said, "Let there be light"; and there was light. Now he would say, "Let there be life in this virgin's womb." And it would be so!

Her love for Joseph would be untouched, unchanged, un-spotted. But what about Joseph's love for her? What would Joseph say when he knew she was carrying a child? What would he do? Would he divorce her? Would he let her be stoned to death?

She could not tell Joseph the child was the son of God. She could not tell anyone. Who would believe her? She knew what the women at the well would say, how they would look at her, how they would laugh, how they would smirk at Joseph!

But God was asking this of her. He was asking it solemnly, through one of his holy angels. She could hesitate no longer. She answered gladly, freely, fervently:

"Behold the handmaid of the Lord; be it done to me according to thy word!"

Then all the angels sang *Hosannas*. The world had been given a new life, a new opportunity. A new era had begun with the first Hail Mary. The Word was made flesh, and dwelt within Eve's daughter.

Gabriel prostrated himself again at Mary's feet, for he beheld the Triune God descending on her. And he and all the lesser angels sang "Holy, Holy, Holy!"

Joseph's bethrothed had encompassed God, whom not even the sun and the moon and the stars could begin to hold. She had become the mother of Fair Love, the mother of her Creator, the mother of all mankind.

She was still a girl, yet not at all like other girls. For now she held Infinity in her womb. And in her heart there was a sea of sorrow.

CHAPTER III

After a time, a long long time, Mary felt the room too confining for the exultation in her bosom. She covered her hair, stepped softly through the door into the wonder of the night, and climbed the stone stairway to her roof. She stood there, as she had stood before the angel and gazed at the sleeping village. She felt an unusual compassion for its people, an odd new tenderness and concern. There were so many sick people in those little houses, so many discouraged ones, so many wretched poor, so many oppressed, so many sinful souls! They suffered from the tyranny of Caesar; from the murderous hate of Herod; from the greed of the tax collectors; from the stern rules of the priests; from the insolence and malice of the soldiers; and from their own dislike and hatred and distrust of one another.

Her love extended throughout the village, and beyond it, east and west and north and south, to lands unseen and unknown. She was a mother standing over the cradle of a feverish and restless child!

The moon had quartered the horizon since she saw it last; and the few pale stars had grown into millions. Far back of them, above the long ridge of Mount Carmel, a field of emerald stars waved like so many acres of young wheat. North, above the white bandage on the head of Mount Hermon, and east around the brow of Mount Tabor, and south, toward Jerusalem, armies of brilliants moved in solemn processions.

Her Son had made all those bright stars and constellations! And he was moving them now, as though they were puppets, to salute her as the queen of earth and heaven. Truly nothing was impossible to God! Yet how humanly impossible — for the moment — to think of God as a child in the womb. A child in her womb!

A voice softer than a whisper spoke to her: "Some day I shall make the moon a footstool for your feet. And in your crown I shall place the brightest stars in all my galaxies."

Who else but God could use the stars to show his tenderness and love? Who else would know that a woman must be given much more love and comfort after marriage than before?

"Now I shall be more dependent on you than ever, Lord," she said. "And you, beloved, will be entirely dependent on me! On me, the least of all your handmaids. You, maker of a million worlds, will be helpless in my arms!" "How can I bear this responsibility? How can I bear this wondrous mystery?"

"Fear not," the answer came. "I shall be with you always. You are my morning star. You are the herald of a glorious dawn that will come to this slumbering world. The Eternal Sun will not neglect you. Be at peace. The Lord is with thee."

The moon had disappeared, and the morning star had paled. Quietly she descended the stairs. She entered her house to say the prayers prescribed, including the prayer that cries out for the speedy coming of the Savior.

She smiled then, realizing she alone in all the world could say when the Messiah would appear. It was a secret she shared with God and his angels. She must share it with some woman, though. It was too heavy, too divine, to bear alone.

She must see Elizabeth!

Last night when the angel mentioned that dear name, Mary

had known an instant of happiness for her, and had thanked God for her rich blessing. But it was only for an instant; for the crushing ecstasy of the Incarnation had driven all thoughts out of her mind and heart save those of God. Father, Son, and Holy Ghost were working a miracle of love within her; and through their divine meeting she who had been full of grace was filled to overflowing. She was a chalice, a fountain, a torrent, a deluge of grace. And the water of her love had become an intoxicating wine. She had even forgotten Joseph for a time!

Now she must hurry to Elizabeth, to rejoice with her and to to help her in every way she could. She remembered how Elizabeth had been treated by other women, especially those with many children. God had cursed her, they said. That was why she was barren. She, the wife of the holy priest, must have committed many secret sins. Where were those women now? she wondered.

Elizabeth was old. But what were years to God? Had God sent his angel to her too? Did she know she would have a son?

Mary and Elizabeth would have sublime things to discuss. And there would be human problems to solve. She must go at once. But how? She could walk, if she had to. It was a hundred miles or so. The roads were bad. There were often bands of robbers waiting in ambush. But she was young and strong, and God would protect her.

Yet if she went alone, Joseph would suffer cruelly. He might think she had run away and abandoned him. She must let him know she was going, but she could not lie to him. Nor could she say, "My cousin is going to have a son in her old age; an angel told me so." Joseph would not laugh at her; but he would not believe her. Women of Elizabeth's age do not have babies. She could give nobody a reason for her journey.

She decided to leave it all to God. He would arrange everything. She finished her prayers and threw open the door, that she might look at the bright new world — a wedding present from her bridegroom. It was a sparkling dew-drenched world beneath a serene blue sky. And, best of all, Joseph was coming toward her, slowly, leading his donkey. Would he see something new and glorious about her? Would he sense that she was the very nursery of almighty God?

Two women were with him, kin of his, and of Mary's, the daughters of the widow Leah in Ain-Karim. They were probably going home today with the small inheritance their Aunt Rebecca had left them. They were good girls, though ugly and sullen. They had slaved for their aunt for the past two years.

Mary knew she would go with them. She would ride Joseph's donkey. She slipped her feet into a pair of sandals, covered her hair, and went out to welcome her visitors. A new tenderness welled up in her, the tenderness of a mother, the tenderness of God! "My soul doth magnify the Lord! Was ever a woman so blessed as I, to be the spouse and the daughter and the mother of the Lord, and the wife of so glorious a man?"

Ah, but would she be his wife? Would he marry her when the women began to talk about her, when they began openly to insult her? God's will be done!

There was an excitement in Joseph Mary had not expected. Had the Angel Gabriel visited him too? Perhaps not. Yet something supernatural had happened to him; for he was more beautiful, more radiant, more manly, than he had been yesterday. He kept his eyes down, pretending to see nothing, so that the girls who walked beside him might not suspect that the world had changed for him.

He had put a new saddle on the donkey, Mary saw. A woman's saddle. He had covered it with a gay cloth, which was adorned with gold and azure tassels. And he had strung a score or more of new bells in the harness. Sweet bells. Silver bells. Bells with the music of Joseph's love, with the sound of prayer, with the echo of the angel's "Hail full of grace." Where did Joseph get money for these bells?

He had combed the donkey sometime during the night, for the beast had a look of beauty. And it stepped with pride to the jingle of the bells.

"The caravan is getting ready to leave," Joseph said. "Ruth and Rachel will pack your things. And they will go with you."

Mary smiled at the girls. They stared at her, walked past her into the house, and slammed the door behind them. And only then did Joseph meet her eyes. Mary held out her hands to him, that the Power and the Glory and the Love and the Life within her might go out to him first of all the people in the world.

"The Lord has come to Israel," Joseph said, taking her hands in his own and holding them firmly. "The Messiah has been born! Or he will be born very soon! The mountains skip like rams and the hills like the lambs of the flock, for they feel the presence of almighty God. My heart skips too. It skips over hills and mountains, and over valleys lush with the mercy of heaven."

Mary gasped; but she could say nothing. Joseph knew, and he did not know. What was this mystery?

He led her up the path toward his home, then looked down the slope toward the well. The caravan had pitched its tents there sometime in the night. She had not seen it come, nor had she heard it. The camels and asses were resting now. Men were striking the tents, folding canvas, making breakfast. Fires blazed in many places in the road.

Joseph turned away from the sight, and led her through a path that straggled through rocks and patches of wild flowers and weeds. There were lilies in the path, some of them knee high. Many had budded in the night, and one was in flower. The air was still, and daintily perfumed.

"Some day," Joseph said, "perhaps in Ain-Karim, you will find the baby savior of the world, and you will pick him up and hold him to your heart and adore and love him!"

Mary picked a lily bud and put it to her lips. "If I could only tell him I have already found the Baby!" she thought. "If I could only tell him I am the mother of that Child!" She touched the bud to her bosom and put it in Joseph's hands.

"I know what you mean," Joseph said, caressing the bud. " 'Drop down dew, ye heavens, from above and let the clouds rain the Just. Let the earth be opened and bud forth a Savior.' The longing of the world is told in a lily that has not yet opened!"

He laughed at himself then, and at her.

"But I haven't told you how I know," he said, "nor why I am sending you to Ain-Karim. Let us sit down here. We still have time."

He sat on a flat stone and brushed the one beside it, using both hands. He took off the linen scarf that covered his head, and spread it on the clean stone for Mary. When he felt she was comfortable, he began to talk.

"I saw you standing at your door last night, and I wanted to go to you. But I was covered with dirt and dust; and there was a clutter of little boys and girls in my shop who wanted me to fix some broken playthings. While I was working, a very rich and distinguished man came in. A foreigner. A Persian. He seemed to be in no hurry, so I asked him to wait. He sat and watched me, and he watched the children. I liked the man. He had come to buy a cradle. His wife even then was with the midwives, and she would have a boy. He was convinced of that. I gave him the joy of his wish, finished the broken toy, and sent the children scampering away. It was then the man told me of the Messiah, and of Zachary, your cousin Elizabeth's husband."

He stretched out a long arm and picked half a dozen lilies of the valley. He gave them to Mary.

"Nothing on earth smells so sweet," he said, "unless it be your hair."

"Go on," she said, "tell me everything. Is Zachary ill?"

Joseph didn't answer at once. He seemed to be absorbed with the caravan on the road, where the dust now rose like smoke; or with the songbirds trilling in the tree above him, or with the beetle working its slow way through the sand.

"The Persian," he said, "is the son of a merchant. He is a wise man, a student of the stars. He came to Palestine to trade. But he also came to learn what he could of the Messiah. He and many other men in his part of the world know of Daniel's prophecy that the Savior would be born in seventy weeks of years. Those seventy weeks have ended. It is time for the world to rejoice. These men also knew that the Savior would be born in Israel, that he would be the King of the Jews and the Lord of all the world. This Persian called him 'the King of kings and the God of gods.' And he felt it was important to know if he had come to the world, or was soon to come. He said to me, 'I envy you, Carpenter, because your God and King will be born in your country. He may be any boy you see. Perhaps he is already living, though I do not think so, for we have not seen his star. It is possible that the lame little beggar whose toy you fixed is the promised Lord of the world.' "

Joseph scooped up a handful of pebbles and showered them on either side of the beetle so that it must go straight ahead, or turn and hurry back from whence it came.

"The Persian — his name is Cyrus — was in Jerusalem six months or so ago when everyone was talking about the priest who had seen an angel in the Temple, and who had been stricken dumb. The priest was Zachary. Cyrus believed the angel had given Zachary a message about the Messiah; but he waited many weeks, consulting the stars every night, before he went to Ain-Karim. He knew that Zachary could hear a whisper, though he could not utter a sound. He found him in bed, not ill but weak. He asked so many silly questions that Zachary became annoyed, and therefore was an easy victim. Suddenly the Persian asked the one important question. He had waited, like a good swordsman, for the right moment to thrust his blade. And Zachary was helpless. 'Will the Messiah be born before the year is done?' Zachary's eyes said, 'Yes!'

"I asked the Persian if Zachary needed anything. He did not know. I asked about Elizabeth. She was there, he said, but she had avoided seeing him. I suspect she needs friends badly."

He brushed his hands clean and watched the beetle scurry across a patch of sand into a clump of weeds.

"While the Persian and I were talking of the Messiah, a group of his servants entered the shop. They came timidly, as though they expected to be whipped. They informed their master that he was the father of a child, a daughter. He said nothing but they fled.

"He demanded the cradle I had on my workbench. He would not listen to my protests. He poured gold pieces into my hands without counting them, which angered me, a little. Rich men think they can buy anything for gold. He asked me to carve a star on the cradle. The Star of David. For a star would appear in the heavens, he said, when the little God would drop down from those heavens. A bright and blazing star that would bring the whole world to the Baby's bedside! I let the gold lie where I had flung it, and gave the cradle to him. At this he promised to send me bolts of silks and satins for the lining, and soft moleskins, and a bale of white dove feathers which he had not tried to sell.

"His servants returned. Now they were white and shaking. They cringed as they announced that his wife had been delivered of another girl. Poor Cyrus! He grew old and weary as I looked at him. His shoulders drooped. 'Make me a cradle big enough for two,' he said. 'Line it with whatever you have. Put a star on it, if you want to. Make some cushions of the feathers and the satin. I will call for it when my wife is able to travel. We go then to Damascus.'

"I closed my door and ate a few bites — for I was hungry — and said my prayers. I thought I would walk out and look at your house. I thought you might be on your roof, and I might catch a little glimpse of you.

"And he was there. The Persian. In front of my door. He looked young again. And he was on fire. 'Look, Carpenter,' he cried to me. 'Look at the stars! Have you ever seen so many in the skies? Have you ever seen them shine so brilliantly? Have you even seen them dance? Behold, your King and your God has come to this poor cold miserable world at last! And the stars are frantic in their joy.'

"Before I could answer him, his servants came rushing up. This time there was no fear in them. They fairly danced. Like the stars. 'The third one is a boy,' they shouted, 'a beautiful sturdy boy!' I saw tears in the Persian's eyes. He did not bother to wipe them away. He thrust a pouch at me. A pouch of gold. 'You have brought me luck, Carpenter,' he said. 'My son is born, and the Savior of the world is in the womb!' Before I could hand him back his pouch, he was running to his son."

Joseph stood up and extended a helping hand to Mary. He guided her down a steep and narrow ribbon of grit and gravel and dust to the road of the caravans.

"Then I saw you on the roof," Joseph said. "You were wrapped in stars and in starlight. You looked like the queen of the stars, the very queen of heaven. And then, my sister, my spouse, my fairest among all the daughters of Eve, something about you shot through me with such ecstasy that I fell to my knees. Love that is stronger than death is stronger than any man. Your love felled me. It left me so wounded with happiness I could not rise.

I rose when I saw the morning star. And I knew that you must go to Elizabeth and Zachary — and perhaps to the Messiah. Zachary will know about him. Zachary may find him for you, if he is able to leave his bed. Give the child my love and adoration."

"Suppose he has not yet been born," Mary said.

"Then Zachary will find his mother for you. I will join you in Ain-Karim when I can, and bring you home."

"And if I find the woman?" Mary said the words lightly so that Joseph might not know how serious she was.

"Then I will throw myself in adoration at her feet and ask the privilege of kissing her holy hand; for she will be the very throne of God." Joseph thought there were more stars in Mary's eyes than he had seen last night. Aye, and they danced as last night's stars had danced.

Mary laughed joyously, then took the role of a jealous queen addressing her royal Lord. "If you have any lady's hand to kiss," she said, "you may begin with mine!"

Joseph looked at the hand she offered. He dropped to his knees and kissed it reverently. As he did so, Mary bent over him, took from behind his left ear the long curled cedar shaving that proclaimed him a carpenter. She kissed it, and pressed it gently to her bosom. It was more fragrant than the lily bud, or the flowers Joseph had given her. She placed it behind his right ear. And, while he was still on his knees, she brushed her cheek across his uncovered tousled hair.

"I give you the blessing of the Lord, my prince," she said. "May it be with you always."

Joseph was so shaken with the excess of his love he could not rise to help her into the saddle.

His donkey had been placed near the head of the caravan. It bore two great bags of clothing. The widow Leah's girls had brought their donkeys near it. And all was ready. Men were throwing water and sand on the fires, and little feathers of smoke leaped into the growing dust cloud. The last of the asses were being laden; the last ships of the desert were being up-anchored. The smell of the animals was pungent, was rancid. The dust was stinging, blinding.

Mary needed no help. She looked at him as she patted the neck of his donkey, and stroked its beautiful long silky ears. "Farewell," she called. "I will find the woman for you."

He remained on his knees as the caravan began its journey. Overladen beasts of burden went by him, some brushing against his face. White and yellow camels threatened to trample him. Men looked down out of the swirling yellow dust and lashed at him with curses. Yet the feeling of ecstasy remained long in him. And the dust that enveloped him was the dust of many stars.

CHAPTER IV

As she rode through the fields of wild flowers, the dust of stony roads, and the dangerous passages in the hills, Mary wondered and worried about Elizabeth and Zachary, and prayed for them. She expected to see great changes in Ain-Karim. A stricken old man, no doubt — if he were still alive. And a sorrowing, helpless, and frightened old woman. And she was prepared to have her story doubted by either or both of them. Suppose they demanded proof! What proof could she give?

It was a great relief to find them both well and so full of wonder and happiness over the coming of their child that they looked like bride and groom! The greatest change, Mary saw, was in Zachary. He had always been a holy priest, in her memory. But he had been somewhat rigorous, somewhat pompous. At times he was petulant, irritable, fussy. At times he was overbearing; but usually he was shy, reserved, afraid. He liked to stay in a corner, away from people who might slight him. He, like Elizabeth, was used to sneers and insults.

"A priest without a son," he had once said bitterly to Mary, "is as one dead. His name will be forever left out of the registers of the House of Aaron; and there will be no one to pray for him." He added that life was even more painful for a childless wife. "We are dead," he had mourned. "We prayed to the Lord unceasingly, for years, with our faces turned toward Jerusalem. But the Lord did not deign to hear us. Now that we are dead, we have ceased to ask Him for a child. We merely wait for burial."

There was no despondency in him now, no rigidity of any kind, no pompousness, no irritations. He had found God at last; and therefore he had found joy and youth and a sincere love of life. His hair and beard had become a frosty white; but his eyes held the hope and the confidence of a boy, and the humility of a child.

Elizabeth's hair was streaked with gray, but her eyes shone with constant happiness and love. She was the happiest woman in Judea — next to Mary herself. If she yelled at her husband occasionally, it was only because she had forgotten. God had stricken him dumb, but there was nothing wrong with his ears — a hard thing for a woman to remember.

Mary was fearful when she approached the house. She slipped out of the saddle and ran toward the door. "Elizabeth!" she cried. "Zachary! Is anybody home?"

Her cousin came rushing out, arms outstretched, letting her know immediately that all was well.

"Blessed art thou among women," Elizabeth greeted her, taking her fiercely and lovingly into her arms and hugging her. "And blessed is the fruit of thy womb!"

So she knew! How nice of God to let her know! It saved Mary from even the least embarrassment. She kissed Elizabeth. "And how have I deserved that the mother of my Lord should come to me?" Elizabeth demanded.

She dropped to her knees and kissed the hem of Mary's robe. "At the sound of your voice," she whispered, looking up through a mist of shining tears, "the babe in my womb leaped for joy."

Zachary had followed Elizabeth out of the house, but when he saw the women wrapped in each other's arms he knew his welcome would have to wait. He started toward the donkey, which was feasting on the grasses and flowers in the garden, and making a happy riot with his saddle bells. But he forgot the animal when he heard Elizabeth's words. Mary was also pregnant? She was "the mother of my Lord"? And the babe had leaped in Elizabeth's womb at the sound of Mary's voice?

Zachary trembled and fell to his knees. Could it really be so? Was this young girl to be the mother of the Messiah — the Redeemer expected through all the ages of the world?

The Angel Gabriel had told Zachary, six months or so ago, that his son would be filled with the Holy Ghost, even from his mother's womb. Mary's visit had brought the Holy Ghost! The child was sanctified! And so was Elizabeth! How could she have known all these wonderful things unless God had inspired her? And Mary — surely Mary must be overflowing with the Holy Ghost!

He turned slowly to look at her. She was standing beneath a leafy tree, sunshine and shadow playing over her uplifted face. She was tall and regal; which was peculiar, for only a few minutes ago she had been a very little girl. Her clothes were of somber colors, but the dust that glinted on them gave them a golden sheen; and there was something so wonderful about her that Zachary bowed low. He had not knelt to the angel. He could not help prostrating himself before this woman.

For the first time in his life he saw a woman more beautiful than anything around her, more beautiful than anything else in the world. Not even Elizabeth, when he was most in love with her, had made him feel so enraptured. Why, this girl was more beautiful, and more holy, than the Temple itself, the most magnificent building and the holiest place on earth!

The living God was enshrined within her! She was a temple made by God. The ground whereon she stood was holy. He would regard it as a shrine so long as he had breath. Tears of love and happiness flowed down into the thickness of his beard. He felt like a loved and loving child.

Elizabeth's greeting had opened a dam in Mary, behind which she had stored the waters of joy and love and wonder. Now those waters rushed out of her, to flood the world with beauty!

"My soul doth magnify the Lord, and my spirit hath rejoiced in God, my Savior; because he hath regarded the humility of his handmaid; for henceforth all generations shall call me blessed. Because he that is mighty hath done great things to me; and holy is his name. And his mercy is from generations unto generations, unto them that fear him. He hath showed might in his arm; he hath scattered the proud in the conceit of their heart. He hath put down the mighty from their seat, and hath exalted the humble. He hath filled the hungry with good things; and the rich he hath sent empty away. He hath received Israel, his servant, being mindful of his mercy. As he spoke to our fathers, to Abraham and his seed forever."

Zachary looked up, eventually, to see Mary standing above him, a tender smile on her face. She was more lovely, and more holy, than the angel. And he was not at all afraid of her. Rather he felt an absolute trust in her, and a need for her. He realized that he, an old old man, was like a child looking up to its mother!

She was only fourteen or fifteen. Yet there was something wonderfully maternal about her. She extended a hand to him, as though to help him rise. He bent to kiss it, but she was quicker than he. She kissed his hand. And he knew that the Holy Ghost had visited him too, sanctifying him as well as Elizabeth and the baby who would be named John.

Eventually Zachary managed to get up to look after the donkey, which was still merrily ringing its bells and eating Elizabeth's flowers.

He led the animal slowly into the stable, hardly knowing what he did, removed the harness, the saddle, the cloth with the tassels, and the string of little bells. He began to feed and water the beast. And, in his priestly way, he began to wonder about God's purpose in sending Mary here. Was there any connection between her visit, and the visit of the angel to him that day in the Temple? He thought there might be; and he tried to re-capture all the details of his encounter with the angel.

He recalled the trumpets of the priests announcing the morning sacrifice. He heard again the organ as it spread its hundred notes through the Temple and the city, reminding the people that God had a hundred names, one of which was so holy it was known only to a few, and was never pronounced aloud.

He recalled how he felt that morning. He had been afraid, for he had never served at the altar of incense before, and he might make some terrible mistake. He was afraid, also, of being so close to God! He was grateful that he had been chosen for this honor. He had been so long neglected and despised. And he was proud.

He had gone into the holy place slowly, breathing fast. A priest beside him carried incense in a golden vessel. A priest on the other side bore burning charcoal in a silver bowl. He now tried to remember who those priests were. He gave up trying.

He remembered the glint of gold everywhere. On the altar. On the door. On the lampstand and its seven lamps. On the table of shewbread. On the walls. The lamps signified that the light of Israel was God; and the bread that God gave was the life of the people. Was it only by gold, Zachary wondered, that men should honor Life and Light?

He remembered prostrating himself before the veil of the Holy of Holies. He remembered the burning charcoal poured into the golden vessel of incense. He remembered being all alone, and badly frightened. It takes great courage to stand alone in the presence of almighty God. Courage and faith.

He remembered the sudden hush. He was listening for a signal from a priest outside the holy place; he was aware of the lowing of cattle, the bleating of sheep, and the movements and prayers of worshipers somewhere near; but he did not remember whether he had heard the signal or not.

A column of smoke rose from the altar of holocausts, where a lamb was being roasted. It was an unblemished lamb, of course. Its blood had been caught in a golden bowl and sprinkled on the altar. He remembered how he hated the smell of that smoke. And he remembered how he loved the aroma of the incense — a mixture of myrrh and spices, blended according to a recipe given Moses by the Most High. The incense had a powerful odor, and its smoke went straight, and thick, up to the gold-covered roof, and through its vents, directly toward the heavens.

He remembered he had just finished the prayer that implored God to speed the coming of the Redeemer, when he saw the terrifying, beautiful, shining angel!

Zachary, now currying the donkey, could remember perfectly every word the angel had said; just as he would remember perfectly, all the rest of his life, the words of Mary's canticle as she stood beneath the tree.

"Fear not, Zachary, for thy prayer is heard; and thy wife Elizabeth shall bear thee a son, and thou shalt call his name John; and thou shalt have joy and gladness, and many shall rejoice in his nativity. For he shall be great before the Lord; and shall drink no wine nor strong drink; and he shall be filled with the Holy Ghost even from his mother's womb. And he shall convert many of the children of Israel to the Lord their God. And he shall go before him in the spirit and power of Elias; that he may turn the hearts of the fathers unto the children, and the incredulous to the wisdom of the just, to prepare unto the Lord a perfect people."

He remembered that he shook so violently his teeth chattered.

He believed that to see an angel was to die. He was afraid to die. At the same time he was astonished and pleased that God had listened to him, and that he would soon bless the world with his Messiah. He did not know why God had told this news to him, the least of all the priests in the Temple. Perhaps it was to make up for having ignored his prayers for a son.

Then, when the angel told him Elizabeth would have a child — Elizabeth who was barren and old and dead — he was staggered! He did not believe it. He began to argue with the angel, who became angry, and gave his name and his rank to emphasize his rebuke. "I am Gabriel who stand before God, and am sent to speak to thee, and to bring thee these tidings. And behold, thou shalt be dumb, and thou shalt not be able to speak until the day wherein these things shall come to pass, because thou hast not believed my words, which shall be fulfilled in time."

Zachary remembered he had stood before the altar, numb, cold, dazed — trying to bring some order out of the chaos of emotions the angel had stirred in him. Then he went out, still holding the censer. He saw faces he did not recognize. He tried to talk, but he could not utter a word. Somebody took him home, and Elizabeth put him to bed.

Many people had tried to get him to reveal what had happened: but he had told nobody anything — nobody but Elizabeth; and all he had revealed to her was that she would have a son and his name must be John. He had written the words slowly for her, with effort.

But the punishment for his doubt was merciful as well as just, he discovered; for it had kept him from revealing God's secret before God wanted it revealed. God has a time for everything.

Had he not been stricken dumb, Zachary reasoned, he might have babbled to everybody. In which case his little home would have been besieged by armies of curious and vulgar people. Everybody in Judea would have tried to see the old woman who was going to have her first baby. She would have been the prize freak of the world — and she would never have forgiven him.

These past few months had been wonderful. He and Elizabeth had shut themselves up. They had kept away from people. When Elizabeth had had to fetch water from the well, she did it at night, disguised with many robes and veils. And when supplies were needed, Zachary went out for them. Nobody had bothered them. Nobody knew what was happening in their home. They had found peace. They had found each other — after all these sterile years — and they had found real love. These months had been more than a long honeymoon. They had been a renewal of their youth.

Now, suddenly, as he stood with one hand resting on the donkey's back, dismay and agony of mind gripped him like a spasm. Wasn't it possible, he asked himself, that Elizabeth had only imagined Mary was pregnant? That might be! Elizabeth loved her own pregnancy. She thought it the greatest blessing God could give. And she loved Mary, and wanted her to be even more blessed than herself. Why else should she cry out, "Blessed is the fruit of thy womb"? She had not heard from Mary since the girl was espoused to Joseph. That was months ago. And why should she call Mary "the mother of my Lord"? Was it because, knowing her son would have the power and the spirit of Elias, she wanted Mary's son to be greater, to be the Messiah? And suppose the baby had leaped, as Elizabeth claimed, at the sound of Mary's voice! Did that prove it was filled with the Holy Ghost?

The old priest fell to the floor as though he were ill. He writhed in anguish worse than any physical pain. He opened his mouth to pray, and remembered he was dumb. God had punished him for doubting the angel. Was He punishing him now for doubting Mary? Perhaps he was.

"Lord," he pleaded, "turn my heart into that of a child. I am incredulous. Give me the wisdom of the just."

He rose to his feet, blind with tears and unsteady on his feet. He reached out to a beam for support, and touched the ring of bells he had hung upon a peg. And he was calm, remembering Mary as she stood beneath the tree, telling how all generations would call her blessed.

His mind was clear again, and the anguish was healed forever.

"I was trying to make a connection between the visit of the angel and the visit of Mary," he reminded himself, "and I got lost in my own way of arguing, disputing challenging, weighing every word and every fact. And so I blinded myself to the simple truth.

"If God can put life into a dead and sterile womb — and he has done it, and I know full well he has done it — then he can also put life into a virgin womb. And now I know that this is what He has done!

"The angel told me Elizabeth would have a son. I did not believe him. Not until she told me herself. Now the child has been filled with the Holy Ghost, as the angel promised. The Lord who punished me came, riding in the exquisite chariot of his mother's virgin body, to sanctify my boy! And I doubted again! Why? I suppose the fact that she is espoused to Joseph had something to do with it. Yet I know in my heart the child is not any man's. I know he is the very Son of God."

The bells jingled in his shaking hands, and he liked the sound. He patted the donkey affectionately. He laughed at himself.

"You are a wiser ass than I," he said, silently, to the brute. "You never argue about things you do not understand. And you do not base your arguments on lies or suppositions. I assumed that Elizabeth was imagining things because she was a pregnant woman. Yet I was pregnant with foolish ideas. I never told Elizabeth the Messiah could be expected any day. I never told her that John would be great, and that he would have the power and the spirit of Elias. I told her only that she would have a boy, and that his name was John. I forgot this in my zeal to build my doubts into the shape of truth."

He shook the bells again, as though to shake off all foolish and evil thoughts, and hung them back on their peg.

"Aye," he thought, "indeed all ages will call her blessed. All generations will pray with her name on their lips. The name of Mary will hammer forever on the door of heaven, even as the tides smash forever against the rockbound shore. And in all generations there will be many who doubt her and her Child! God have pity on them. Give them the wisdom you have given me, the wisdom of a child."

He went out of the stable to sit in the sunshine and think about God.

CHAPTER V

Joseph arrived in Ain-Karim laden with gifts and accompanied by a shouting, happy, grinning army of young boys. It was late in the afternoon, and Zachary was taking a nap. The noise awoke him.

Joseph had traveled in a caravan to Jerusalem, bringing a few things he thought his betrothed might need. In Jerusalem, after the Passover, he had indulged in a shopping spree. The Persian merchant had paid him well. He bought a goatskin of good wine, three different kinds of cheese, a great quantity of honeycomb, packed in a light wooden box and wrapped with a few rough cloths, a small keg of pickled fish, a leg of lamb, and six loaves of the best bread he could find in the bazaar. These articles, with force and skill, he crammed into a saddle-bag he had bought at a bargain. And, just before he set out for Ain-Karim he purchased a live chicken. He managed, with help, to get the bag containing Mary's things securely settled on his back. The saddlebag he carried suspended from his right shoulder. The chicken he carried by the legs in his left hand.

The way was longer than he remembered and there were many steep hills. He could not run all the way, as he had intended to. Frequently he had to stop and rest. He was not exactly tired, he told himself, he was just out of breath.

He was nearing his goal when the boys saw him. They howled with mirth. They danced around him, mocking him. "Here's a man that is his own donkey," one said. "Who's got a whip to make the donkey go?"

Joseph laughed with them. He spoke to them kindly. They didn't understand his Galilean accent; but they understood him. Within a few minutes he was taking things out of the saddlebag and giving them to his tormentors to carry for him. They fought for the privilege of carrying the weightier articles. When each had something to carry, Joseph gave the word, and the group went forward, singing and shouting.

Outside Zachary's house Joseph relieved the boys, piled the wares neatly on the steps, and reached an arm deep into the sack that contained Mary's things. He brought forth a cloth bag of pistachio nuts, and was about to distribute them when he noticed that a dozen or more new boys had assembled around him. He gave the bag to one of the boys and bade him share it with his friends.

It was at this point that Zachary, fearful that he was being invaded by curious neighbors, and that his wife's secret would be known, charged out of the house, scowling as fiercely as his benevolent face would let him. Joseph, still clutching the chicken by its legs, raised it in a sort of salute. The bird squawked and cackled in terror. Zachary stepped back.

"Hail Zachary," Joseph cried. "It's Joseph, the poor carpenter from Nazareth. God be with you and your house. I've brought you a little keg of fish. Right out of the Sea of Galilee. Pickled by Zebedee, 'Old Thunderhead' himself. I remembered how you love them. But the boy who carried it had a collision with the boy who carried the honey. Maybe the fish will be too sweet, or the honey too bitter."

By this time Zachary had recognized his visitor and taken him in his arms. He made signs that Joseph was to go into the house and let the parcels stay where they were. He must bathe his hands and face. It was amazing, Joseph thought, how easily Zachary could make himself understood. Zachary took the hen from him, smoothed its feathers gently, and started with it toward the stable.

Joseph had washed his face and hands when Elizabeth came in from her garden. "Mary's Prince Joseph!" she cried. "You are more than welcome. Let me get a towel. We have waited so long and so patiently for you! What kept you? Here! Dry yourself and let me kiss you."

She kissed him on both cheeks, gave him a gentle and motherly hug, ran a hand lightly through his thick hair, snatched the towel from him, and dried a few wet spots he had missed. "Sit there," she bade him, pointing to a chair, "and let me take off your sandals. I will fetch water in a second. Mary will be so glad to see you. She's gone to the well." She flung open the door and saw a pile of groceries, and Zachary carrying a chicken in his hand.

"Zachary," she screamed. "Joseph's here. Don't kill that chicken now. Wait a day or two. And tell that ass to stop braying!"

She returned, vigorously, to Joseph and his needs. "How that poor man has put up with me all these years I don't know. He could have divorced me years ago, and married a woman who would give him children. But he loved me too much, the idiot! You must be tired, Joseph, carrying all that load! What a strong young man you are."

Joseph sat, or rather slumped, in the proffered chair, and stretched and yawned. Elizabeth disappeared. Zachary brought in the honey and then the keg of fish. He was old, Joseph knew; yet he looked absurdly young for hair so white. Elizabeth was strangely young too. But hadn't she put on weight? No. It wasn't a matter of weight with her. Joseph sat up straight. He almost sprang up onto his feet. The dear old woman was going to have a child!

So that was why the Persian had not seen her! She had hidden herself so he wouldn't see her condition. That was why the house had looked so deserted. Elizabeth must have barred out all her neighbors! She was sixty or more, and — this was a miracle indeed!

He thought of the angel who appeared to Zachary. He thought of the Persian's thundering news that the Messiah would soon be born — that he was in the womb! Elizabeth's womb, of course! Elizabeth would be the mother of God!

He had asked Mary to find the mother of the Child — and, lo, she had led him here! And here he sat, lazy and helpless, letting that holy woman remove his sandals! Awe held him where he was. Awe chilled him. Awe made him as dumb as Zachary.

What should he do? Get up and kneel before her? He wanted to, but her hands were on his feet; and it would be awkward to do anything at all. Besides, there was a blessing in her hands. He should feel shame, letting her touch his grit-filled dirty sandals. But he felt no shame at all. The awe that had frozen him now warmed and heartened him.

Elizabeth laughed. Joseph had never heard her laugh before. He had seldom seen her smile. She had always been a sad, silent, suffering, sweet, resigned old woman. Now she laughed like a bride, with a gay tinkle in her voice. That was another strange thing, because she was in the next room! How could she be there, and here at his feet, at the same time?

He looked down. It was not Elizabeth who had taken off his sandals. It was Mary. And she was holding them against the spotless white of her apron as though they were precious! And her eyes were shining on him!

She had a napkin on her shoulder, and a basin of water by her side. She was robed in something gold and brown. She wore no veil. Her hair rippled gloriously back from her forehead and flowed halfway down the arch of her back.

He looked at her dazedly, wondering when she had come in, and why he had neither seen nor heard her. He forgot Elizabeth. He forgot his urge to kneel before her as before the holiest of shrines. He forgot his tiredness, his hunger. He forgot everything except his love for this woman who didn't care whether or not his filthy sandals soiled her new white apron.

"I live again," he said. "When you went away I perished. When you went away, God went with you and I died. I died in a cloud of dust. But I died happily, for I had kissed your hand. Nazareth was dark and cold and empty.

"Now God has come back. He is at home in you, my love, my dove, my Mary undefiled. He looks at me through your eyes!"

Mary put down the sandals, but kept looking at Joseph. And she began, like a good Jewish wife, lovingly, to wash his tired, dusty feet.

"And again," Joseph said, "I have the impulse to kneel and kiss your hand."

Elizabeth, carrying a steaming dish to the table, overheard him. "Let Mary finish washing and drying your feet. Let her purify your hands. Then bless the food and eat. I hope your appetite is good."

Joseph did not hear a word she said. He was not really aware she was in the room. But automatically he obeyed her. He ate as though he had been starved; yet he managed to talk as he ate.

Zachary was enjoying himself as Joseph ate. The way the young man wrestled with his food had made him think of Jacob wrestling with an angel. This led him into a recollection of the Angel Gabriel. Gabriel was a blinding light, that moved so as to give the impression of great shimmering wings. He had a countenance of glory rather than any sort of human face. He

had power! And he had a burning love! Zachary had been
seared by the fire of that love.

There was the same angelic power in Joseph, the old priest
thought. And some of the angel's love of God was in him too,
otherwise the Lord would never have chosen him to protect and
rear his Son. Perhaps Joseph, who loved to laugh and to make
others laugh, who loved to eat, and to labor, and to run to his
beloved with a donkey's load of groceries on his back — perhaps
Joseph was greater in Jehovah's eyes than any spirit who stood
before the throne.

The grace of God could lift a mortal high above immortal
choirs. Mary, because she would be the virgin mother of God,
the mother of Perfection, must give God more joy than all the
legions of angels. And Joseph? Zachary decided that, because
he would be the foster father of God, he might well outshine any
angel of God. He too was a virgin, Elizabeth had informed him.
Zachary was amazed at that.

Zachary felt humble in Joseph's presence. He asked himself
if he would have surrendered Elizabeth, in her youth, as gener-
ously as Joseph had surrendered Mary. He remembered how
beautiful his bride had been. He shook his head. No. He could
not have done that. If Elizabeth had wanted to remain a virgin
he would have left her. He would never have taken a vow of
chastity. His love had been only as big as himself. Joseph's
love — what could one compare it to?

There had been men in Israel, he knew, who had forsworn
women. But not one of them had been motivated by such pure
love as Joseph's. Perhaps in all the history of the world no other
young man had ever chosen to be a virgin because he was madly
in love with a woman; and with God!

Elizabeth, meantime, removed the dishes when Joseph had
emptied them. She refilled them and brought them back.

Joseph was completely unaware of her attendance on him,

nor of Zachary's beaming approval. There was nothing in the world for him except the light in Mary's eyes. Yet he spoke of people in Nazareth and showed them in comic kindly lights. He narrated incidents that had happened during his trip to Jerusalem. He made Elizabeth and Mary laugh, and Zachary grimace and smile. And when he was sated, and somewhat normal again, he paid Elizabeth a compliment he sincerely meant.

"I ate too much and too wolfishly," he said. "But I couldn't help it. Every bite was a prayer of thanks. God bless the cook who uses so well the talents given her, and who knows that food should please not only the palate but also the eye and the nose — and sometimes the ear as well. We can give thanks for a crust of bread and a cup of water, of course. And we should; for all things come from God. But when the Lord gives one a banquet like this, one cannot help singing a hymn of praise. A cook, like you, Cousin Elizabeth, must bring many hymns of praise to God."

Elizabeth, giggling like a schoolgirl, said to Zachary, "He thinks I am a good cook. He doesn't know Mary prepared this dinner for him."

"Who baked the bread?" Joseph asked.

"Mary," Elizabeth said.

"I need a place to stay," Joseph said to Mary, "until I take you home."

"The widow Leah needs some repairs on her house," Mary said. "She has a little money now, and can afford to give a good carpenter a room, two meals a day, and a few pieces of silver."

"Is the house far away?"

"It is near the well," Mary said with a little smile.

"And has my room a view of the well?"

"Oddly enough," Mary assured him, the smile widening, "it has an excellent view of the well."

"And a woman going to the well," Elizabeth said, "might drop in to see how the work was going, being sorry for the widow and wanting to be certain she was not cheated by the carpenter. The widow will feed you well, Joseph; but she will question you as though she were a judge and you a prisoner. Don't tell her anything about me."

"I'll take you there," Mary said, reaching for a veil to cover her hair. Joseph rose and stood beside her. And Elizabeth stood before the two of them, a look of exaltation changing her face and form. She was erect, stern, resplendent, a seeress, a woman filled — Mary thought — with the love and the wisdom and the vision of the Lord.

"God will bless you both," Elizabeth said. "You have given up all rights to having children; yet I know that even when I hold my firstborn in my arms, I shall not be nearly as happy as you will always be. You have each taken a vow of chastity. Neither of you mentioned it. But I know. And through that vow you will beget centuries of children! God promised Abraham more descendants than the sands in the seashore or the stars in the sky; but your children will outnumber his a thousandfold; for chastity is most fruitful before God!

"Sarah was ninety when she knew she would become a mother. She heard the Lord tell her husband so. She laughed. I didn't laugh. I wept. I wept for joy. I had nagged and henpecked and scolded God into giving me a child. I was grateful. Yet I was somewhat resentful too, because He had made me wait. I am a selfish old woman who wanted her own will. I think God answered my prayers not only because he has some purpose in mind for my son — but also because he tired of my whining."

Joseph could no longer restrain himself. He knelt and kissed the hem of her robe. He kissed her calloused, hardened, wrinkled hand; and he looked up at her with the utmost reverence. "I came to take Mary as soon as possible," he said. "But I

didn't know how much you needed her. I will take the room with
the view. I will work for the widow; and perhaps for other people
in Ain-Karim. And I will come here often. For God lives here."

Elizabeth looked at the young man through a fog of tears.
Nobody else had ever kissed her hand. Not even Zachary. "God
bless you, Mary's prince," she said. "Go to the widow's. But
tell her nothing!"

The old couple watched the young couple strolling slowly
along the path, remembering days when they too were young.

CHAPTER VI

Life was quiet in Ain-Karim. To Joseph it was exciting too. Mary scrubbed, dusted, swept, cooked, washed, and dried the dishes and put them away, attended to the laundry, helped Elizabeth make clothes for her baby, took care of the donkey, and went on many errands. But always she seemed to be the same; for, Joseph believed, she was forever in the presence of God. Nothing could excite or depress her.

Joseph's day was filled with change. He worked happily and swiftly, when his mind was on his task. Sometimes, when he remembered how dear Mary was to him, he stood or sat, motionless. Sometimes, when he returned to the remembrance of his duty, he found the widow Leah and one or both her daughters staring at him out of sullen and suspicious eyes. There was a hostility in them that he could feel. He pitied them. They were the ugliest women in Herod's kingdom, and they were jealous of Mary's beauty, and her grace, and her goodness of heart. They hated her. He realized this one day when he was watching, enraptured, as Mary filled her pitcher at the well. He had turned, at some noise they made, to see the malice in their faces.

He wanted to talk to them about Mary. But he had stopped speaking to them, for whenever he did so they returned to their eternal questions: "How is the wicked priest the angel punished? . . . How is that sinful old woman, and why has she shut herself away from all her friends and neighbors? . . . Does she realize, at last, that she isn't good enough for us? . . . What is she doing? . . . Why did you and your wife come to help her?" When Joseph had discovered that they did not want answers to their questions he resorted to shrugs, gestures, silence. He was always good-humored in their presence. He always had a friendly smile for them — or so he believed. He always tried not to show his pity for them.

As soon as the sun went down Joseph would take off his working clothes, wash his hands and face, don a clean robe, and hurry to the home of Zachary. It was, he thought, like going to heaven every evening. The worse the day, the more marvelous the night! There was good food in that humble dwelling, perfect cooking, much harmony, much pure love; and hours of talking about God! And there was happy work in the making of a cradle.

One night late in June, after he had returned to the widow's home, Joseph was awakened by a knock on the door and the sound of Mary's voice. He dressed quickly, and ran to open the door. It was already open, and Mary stood there, beset by the widow and her daughters. "What do you want of him?" they were demanding, all with one bad-tempered voice, all with accusing eyes.

Joseph looked at them, and they stepped back and let him pass. He knew what errand had brought Mary to him. He did not have to ask her any questions. He hurried to the midwife Elizabeth had chosen. Mary went on to the well.

Joseph did not return to his rooming house that night. He spent most of the time with Zachary. Zachary was now a limp old man who sat in a dark corner and mopped his face and hands every little while. Whenever Elizabeth cried out in her agony, he covered his wet face with his wet hands, as though he were guilty of a crime.

Early in the morning, the baby cried. Zachary leaped out of his chair and fell on his knees to thank God for his son. It was some little time before he could compose himself and go to see the baby.

"My son," Elizabeth called out. "Let me see my son!"

Joseph was thrilled at the jubilation in her voice; and at the lusty and continued crying of the child.

He did not know it was the voice of John the Baptist, "the voice of one crying in the wilderness; Make straight the way of the Lord." He thought of it as the voice of the Savior. He prostrated himself in adoration, and in love and joy.

Someone pounded on the door. Joseph looked out the window. A woman was there, popeyed and panting. Another woman joined her, another and another and another, half dressed, half awake, half crazy to know whose baby had been born.

John the Baptist had shaken Ain-Karim as, years later, he would shake the world.

The widow Leah almost clawed Joseph when she heard the news. "I am the last woman in the village to be told," she wailed. "The very last. You could have told me last night. Then I would have been the first. The Lord curse you and your woman. May the child she is bearing be as dumb as the evil priest the angel so justly punished."

"And may the Lord forgive you," Joseph said, "and may he give you peace." He packed his tools and what few belongings he had, and went to find another room. He prayed for the woman as he walked, and for her two poor homely girls.

Zachary's home could no longer be compared to heaven; for the crowds of people who forced their way in, day and night, brought turmoil and argument and hate. Yet many friends rejoiced with Elizabeth and Zachary. A few scolded and abused Elizabeth for keeping her secret from them. Some who had despised her for her barrenness, despised her because she had

given birth in "her silly old age." She had had the baby to spite
them, they said. She had had it in secrecy, "like a wayward girl,"
simply to show her contempt for them!

Even the cool beauty of Mary, and the shining happiness in
the old-new mother, did not serve to stop the wrangling in the
house when Elizabeth said the baby would be called John.
Nobody in her family, nor Zachary's, had been called John.
This child must — and would, friends assured her angrily — be
called Zachary, after his father. It made no difference what she
wanted. Who ever heard of a mother giving a child a name?
She was a stubborn old woman, but she must submit.

Zachary, dressed in his priestly robes, settled the matter forever. He wrote a message for all those who could read. "His
name is John."

Zachary knew then that his name would be entered in the
register of the House of Aaron, and that he would have a prophet
to pray for him; but he could not know his name would be
written in imperishable ink, and with the brightest colors — nor
that his son's name would be known and esteemed and loved
so long as the world endured.

Joseph was standing near the baby's cradle, with Mary, when
he heard the dumb priest speak. He recognized the voice at once.
But he was too affected to turn around. He still thought John
was the Messiah. And he was sure the baby had performed a
miracle for his father. He had removed the angel's ban. He had
made the dumb speak. Now, Joseph expected, the priest would
reveal the angel's secret! Then all present would adore the child
and sing hymns of thanks to the Most High!

Zachary's first words tended to confirm Joseph's belief. He
closed his eyes that he might listen better.

"Blessed be the Lord, the God of Israel, because he hath
visited and wrought the redemption of his people; and hath
raised up for us a horn of salvation in the house of David, his

servant; as he promised through the mouth of the holy prophets who were from the beginning; that he would save us from our enemies and from the hand of all that hate us; to show forth his mercy to our fathers and remember his holy Covenant; the oath that he swore to Abraham, our father, that he would grant unto us that, being delivered from our enemies, we might serve him without fear, in holiness and justice before him, all the days of our life."

Zachary paused for a long breath, and walked to the cradle for a better look at his son.

"And thou, O child," Zachary prophesied, "shalt be called a prophet of the Most High; for thou shalt go before the face of the Lord to prepare his ways; to give knowledge of salvation to his people, for the remission of their sins; through the bowels of the mercy of our God, wherein, rising from on high, he hath visited us; to enlighten them that sit in darkness and in the shadow of death, to direct our feet into the ways of peace."

The elation in Joseph dimmed. This child was not the Messiah. He managed to leave the crowded room, taking Mary with him.

"Do you remember a verse in Malachy?" she asked him. Without waiting for an answer, she quoted it: "Behold I send an angel, and he shall prepare the way before my face. And presently the Lord whom you seek, and the angel of the testament whom you desire, shall come to his temple. Behold he cometh, saith the Lord of Hosts."

"Almost the words of Zachary," Joseph said. "An angel who will go before the face of the Lord to prepare his ways. And the Lord is coming!"

"He is coming to his temple," Mary said softly. "Behold he cometh. And you shall kneel at the foot of his temple and adore him. Indeed, you shall even hold him in your arms, Joseph, my prince!"

Mary and Joseph returned to Nazareth when Elizabeth no longer needed them. They traveled lightly, Joseph having given away many of his gold pieces, and Mary most of her clothing. They went quickly, and happily. Yet, even when he was most happy, Joseph was troubled. A jealous and malicious woman had made him wonder and fear.

And other women added to his growing misery. They came into his shop for ridiculous reasons or no reasons at all. They asked questions that had no meaning. And they smiled or snickered at his answers. They were mysterious and subtle and sly. There was no viciousness in them, Joseph knew, but they were as merciless, in their way, as the widow Leah.

Joseph had noticed, of course, that Mary's lovely figure was sweetly swelling, as though it held a child. But he thought his eyes were lying or that his vision had been infected by the poisonous insinuations of many women.

Yet facts are facts, he realized, and must be faced. Not even the most ardent lover, or the most foolish, can hide himself from facts. And the fact was that Mary was going to become a mother!

In the light of tragedy, in the clear air of hopelessness, a lover can see clearly. He may know what to do. And he may not. He may be helpless to do anything. Love, like life, is sweetest when it is most endangered; most prized when it is soon to vanish. But sometimes a man must sit idly by and let both life and love abandon him forever!

One fact threatened Joseph with imminent disaster. Another consoled him, even while it tantalized and puzzled him. Mary, in some ways, had not changed at all! She still held all heaven in her eyes. She still made a man feel holy just by coming near him. She still loved him tenderly and chastely, and let him see it. He could no more doubt her integrity than he could doubt the goodness and the purity of God.

These two facts faced each other in deadly combat, each as strong and convincing as the other; and they fought for the complete possession of his mind. He could not reconcile them. He could not explain them. Mary was still a virgin! Mary would soon become a mother!

His faith in her might have helped him solve the riddle; but he had not yet shaken off his belief that Elizabeth was the mother of the Christ. And perhaps Mary was too close to him, and too dear to him, to be regarded as the woman chosen by almighty God.

All he knew was that an avalanche of jagged stones was beginning to fall between himself and his beloved. There had been only a few stones so far, and they had cut and bruised him badly. But presently God would loose a whole mountainside of little stones into the gap he had already made; and life and love would depart, with no hope of their ever coming back.

Joseph was wise enough to know that God puts barriers between a woman and a man, so that they might test their love. Through such a challenge, the lovers' appreciation of each other would increase; they would know, much better than before, how much they needed one another. They would learn that love thrives in rocky soil; that what separated them physically might unite them emotionally; and that what kept them apart might wed and weld them spiritually together in a mystic marriage. The knowledge that there was a barrier between them might spur them to heroic efforts that would turn the barrier into straw.

But Joseph was afraid God meant this barrier to be a permanent one. God was displeased with him, he thought. He didn't know any reason for God's anger, but there must be one. His holy will be done!

Joseph remembered he had promised to be the caretaker of the garden, the guardian of the fountain. He had failed! How terribly he had failed. Yet the garden had never looked so peaceful, so blessed, so sublimely lovely. The water of the fountain had never been so gay, so sparkling, so clean and pure. Nor had it ever made such happy music.

Joseph had failed; but God had not. Perhaps it was Joseph's presumption that had angered the Lord, his naïve belief that God needed him to protect this woman so very dear to him. God had let this happen for some divine purpose. So it must be good.

He roamed the hills about the town at night. He sat for hours on a rock or a tree stump, looking at Mary's house — and at his own which would never shelter her. He slept little. He could not work. He avoided people. He avoided Mary, though he ached to see her. And he prayed constantly for guidance, for wisdom, for some clue to what the Lord expected of him.

One night, in the darkness of his shop, mechanically rocking the cradle he had made with such love and happiness, he came to a decision. He would give her up to God. He would put her away privately and thus prevent any hint of scandal. No one would reproach her, believing her child was Joseph's, which she had a right to bear. They would condemn Joseph for deserting her and the baby. They would regard him as too base to speak to, as one dead and unmourned. He would be the unhappiest man who ever lived. Worse than that, he would never see Mary again — nor ever look upon her child.

He was like Adam, now, he thought. For, through an act of his own will, he had barred himself from paradise forever. The angel of his promise was stationed outside the gate, with a fiery sword, to keep him in exile.

He shivered. It was cold in the room. He noticed his face was wet with tears. He wanted to get up, wash, undress, and go to bed. But there was no strength in him. He remained on his knees, rocking the cradle. What should be done with the clumsy thing? It would embarrass him to offer it to Mary. It would embarrass her to accept it. Why couldn't he put his tormented soul and body into the merciful depths of unconsciousness? Why did he bother about a cradle?

He fell asleep on his knees.

And in his dream an angel came to him and told him not to be afraid to marry the girl he loved, for the Child growing in her was the very Son of God; and that his name should be Jesus, "for he shall save his people from their sins."

The unexplainable had been explained. The irreconcilable facts had been reconciled. Mary was still a spotless virgin. Mary was with Child. Joseph, out of love for God, and out of love for Mary, had given her back to God. God had returned her; and with her, his own divine Son.

What mortal could outdo God in love or generosity?

Joseph woke, and rendered praise to God. Now he knew what Mary had meant when she said she would find "the woman" for him. Now he knew that, all these months, she had been trying to reveal her secret to him. And he had been too dense, too stupid, too masculine, to realize she had a secret.

He sang aloud while he bathed himself: "Drop down dew, ye heavens, from above and let the clouds rain the Just. Let the earth be opened and bud forth a Savior."

He was almost disgusted with himself; but he was too happy to be disgusted with anything. Some months ago he could have known that Mary was the mother of his God — and her God!

How wonderful a thought!

He should have guessed it when she put the bud into his hand. He remembered his words to her: "The longing of the world is told in a lily that has not yet opened." But he was too full of the Persian then, and of excitement about the Messiah.

He reconsidered that. He was wrong. He was not too full of the Persian. He was not full enough. For now — only now — he remembered something he had neglected to tell Mary.

"You Jews," the Persian had said, somewhat bitterly, "are so positive the Savior will be born of an ordinary marriage that you rush into wedlock as soon as you are weaned. Every one of you wants to be the mother or the father of the Christ! Everywhere else in the world, people know that the Saint of saints will be born of a virgin."

"I have heard nothing of this, and I have been carefully taught," Joseph had answered somewhat stiffly. "Did Daniel say that?"

The Persian had shaken his head. He didn't know. Perhaps it was Isaias or some other prophet. But all the world outside of Palestine had heard the prophecy. He saw he had nettled Joseph. Therefore he was kinder than he might have been; and hearing that Joseph was espoused to the most beautiful girl in Nazareth — or all of Galilee — he placed a string of silver bells on his workbench.

"Foolishly enough, I had hoped to find the little God already born, in Jerusalem itself, perhaps, or somewhere close to it; and I had this present for Him. Please take it, Carpenter, for your own firstborn. Or some happy day, if it is you who finds the Saint of saints, you will have the privilege of giving him these bells."

Joseph hurried into his best clothes, intending to go at once to his beloved. But first he had to read Isaias. Yes. It was there. . . . "Hear ye therefore, O house of David . . . the Lord himself shall give you a sign. Behold, a virgin shall conceive and bear a son and his name shall be called Emmanuel."

He shouted with pure joy.

He picked up the cradle and ran with it down the path to Mary's open door.

He had made a cradle for the incarnate Son of God, but the Most High had made a cradle too. One infinitely more beautiful. And she was probably waiting for him, just behind the door!

CHAPTER VII

The marriage of Mary and Joseph was not nearly so gay as the marriage at Cana. There were not as many guests. There wasn't as much to eat or drink. But there was more real happiness; there was more modesty, and there was more love. The ceremony was performed some time before Caesar Augustus decreed that a census should be taken of "the whole world"; and that every Jew should register in his own city.

Joseph rebelled, asking if he were an ox or an ass to be counted as one of Rome's possessions, and demanding to know why a poor man should be forced to go all the way to Bethlehem simply to give his name to a tax collector. Mary reminded him that heaven was using Caesar for its own ends. It was written that the Child should be born in Bethlehem, the city of David. Joseph was sure God spoke through Mary. He listened to her. He would have listened anyway, for with just a look she still made the blood rush singing through him; she still brought tears to his eyes.

They decided not to join a caravan. They must be alone on this journey. It would be a honeymoon. It would be a pilgrimage, the holiest sort of pilgrimage. They could share it with no one. They knew all the dangers lurking in ambush for them. But the Holy One of Israel was with them. What was there to fear?

It was winter, the rainy season. The roads were horrible —
treacherous, narrow, pitted with ugly holes. The way went up
and down and around many hills and mountains — raw rocks
that stood like lepers begging for the alms of a traveler's attention. Gray rocks, yellow, dirty brown, sickly white, all marked
with old and hideous scabs and scars. A few exhibited thin ill-
nourished trees or shamefully scraggly bushes, but most were as
God made them and time marred them. They had never
mothered so much as a patch of moss.

When the rain stopped and the sun shone, the wet hills flashed
with splendor. But they resumed their depressing mood when
the rain began again. If they wore rainbows, and they did now
and then, they wore them carelessly.

Joseph, leading the donkey, constantly worried about his wife.
She was well wrapped, and he had brought plenty of extra clothes
that the rain could not reach. But there was always a chance she
might suffer a chill. The Lord was with her, he knew; yet a man
must make a fuss in spite of that, he mustn't expect the Lord
to assume all the responsibility. He was constantly seeking a
place of shelter, especially when he saw the rain was not going
to keep on drizzling but was going to pour. Somehow he always
found a cave in time, a place where they could rest, eat, pray,
watch the downpour, and wait until it was safe to proceed.

"There must be an angel with us," Joseph said. "He always
gets us to a dry place in time."

Mary laughed, and the world was filled with splendor.

"One angel for the Son of God?" she said. "Surely his Father
would give him a legion or more."

The rain was nothing to Mary, Joseph thought. She didn't feel
it. She didn't see it. She was riding through a road in Eden where
rain never fell; but Eden never saw a lass so lost to love as she.
The bells around her saddle expressed but little of the joy he saw
in her eyes and heard in her voice.

Every now and then, when it was drizzling or when it was dry, Joseph lifted his voice in a hymn; and the bells on the donkey chimed merrily in with him:

"Drop down dew, ye heavens, from above, and let the clouds rain the Just. Let the earth be opened and bud forth a Savior. . . . And as the rain and the snow come down from heaven, and return no more thither, but soak the earth and water it, and make it to spring, and give seed to the sower, and bread to the eater; so shall my word be, which shall go forth from my mouth; it shall not return to me void, but it shall do whatsoever I please, and shall prosper in the things for which I sent it."

They went slowly. Joseph, barefooted and bent with the great burden on his back, splashed carelessly through the many dirty pools of water. The ass walked daintily and with care, as though he knew he carried the Treasure of the world.

The first night, just before the sun went down, they found an inn, a caravansary, that looked clean; and as they were, providentially, the only patrons, they spread their mats upon a scrubbed wooden platform and spent the night. Joseph cared for the donkey before he prepared his bed. Mary went immediately to sleep.

The next night, and the night that followed, the inns were crowded, and the travelers found refuge in a cave.

On the fourth night they entered Bethlehem. It was cold and raining lightly. And it was getting dark.

"Sing joyfully to God, all the earth," Joseph sang. "Make melody. Rejoice and sing. Sing praise to the Lord on the harp. Make a joyful noise before the Lord, our King. . . . Behold thy Savior cometh."

The town swarmed with people. Joseph halted the donkey in front of the nearest stall in the marketplace, that of a grocer and baker, and bade the beast to stay there. He chose the place because its roof had an overhang that would keep the rain from

Mary, and because he had seen the fire in the oven. Mary would have warmth as well as protection from the rain.

"I am Joseph of Nazareth," he said to the grocer, an old man with faded brown hair and beard. "I go to the inn to see if there is room, but I shall return for bread and cheese and a skin of wine, and perhaps a few dates or figs. You will be open?"

The grocer looked up from a much thumbed copy of Genesis, and in the nervous light of the torches and the timid light of the oil lamps, Joseph noted that his eyes were curiously young and mild. "I am Nathan of Bethlehem," he said. "I will wait. And the lady and the beast are not in the way." His smile was warm and shy; and Joseph's worry lessened.

From her perch on the donkey's back, Mary studied the grocer and the baker; the used-up and benevolent old man, and the tall and sturdy young man who stood revealed every now and then in the fire shining out of the oven door. He was kind too, she realized — for it was evident he opened the door many times when he put no bread into the oven nor took any out. He wanted the fire to take the damp and the chill from her. She blessed him and his father. She was sure the old man was the father.

These men were different from all the other people in the vicinity. There was a drunken woman across the street. There were drunken men too, some of them shouting vulgarities. There were Roman soldiers, haughty and hard. There were weary travelers on horses, camels, and asses. There were furtive bands of little thieves. Her heart winced at the sight of them.

Joseph came striding through the rain. The sight of him gave her more inner warmth than the oven blaze that had dried her clothing. She knew what he would say. And she was glad. She had had a glimpse of the inn and its people. She could not help shuddering at the thought of having her Baby in such a sordid and noisy and overcrowded place.

"No room in the inn," Joseph said. "No room anywhere. Every family has guests or boarders. But there are caves near here. I think I can still find them. I used to play in them when I was a child."

"It is God's will," Mary said. At the sound of her voice the grocer put aside his parchment and looked at her, and the baker put away the long wooden spade that fed the oven, and took a few steps forward.

"When Adam and Eve were driven out of Eden," Mary said, "they found themselves in an unknown and hostile world. Adam didn't know what to do or where to go. There were no houses or stores. He had to build some sort of shelter. But he had no tools, and he wouldn't have known how to use them. God pitied him and showed him a hole in a rock, one big enough for him and Eve and all the children they might bear. All our civilizations have come out of that cave." And to Joseph she whispered, "Why should he not provide just such a home for his Son, since he comes to bring all the children of Adam and Eve back to paradise?"

"It will be cold in the cave," Joseph said. "And dark. And filthy. And foul smells may linger there. Have you firewood, Nathan of Bethlehem, and oil?"

As he spoke he noticed a small group of children drawing close. They were streaming rain. They were barefooted. They were ragged. They looked thin, starved. One of them, a boy of nine or ten, had a rock in each of his dirty hands.

At the same time Mary saw a larger band of children approaching stealthily from the opposite direction. She sensed what was in their minds. The small group would beg. The grocer would refuse. They would throw stones and run away, hoping the grocer and his son would chase them. Then the main group would rush in and steal everything they could carry. The smell of the fresh-baked bread, and the cheery light and warmth of the oven fire had tempted them beyond all power to resist. She saw that one of the boys in the larger group was sobbing.

She slipped off the donkey and ran to him. She was no longer tired nor cold, nor damp, nor stiff. She picked up the boy and hugged him. She put him down and found a square of linen cloth inside her mantel, and wiped the tears and the dirt from his face. And all the time she talked to him in such sweet and tender accents that he began to cry afresh.

"I ain't hurt," he said. "I'm just hungry."

"You're all hungry," Mary said, raising her voice and looking at all the others. "And there is bread! However, God does not want you to steal it. Stealing is a great sin. But letting children go hungry and ragged and unloved is a greater sin."

She heard Joseph say to Nathan: "I'll need a dozen or more loaves. That bread that smells so good. And the biggest cheese you have. And those good-looking figs and dates. And what about sweets?"

Mary had noticed the sweets. They were old and stale and flyspecked, and poisonously dyed. "I have some little cakes in the bundle on your back," she said to her husband, loud enough for all the children to hear. "I made them myself. Honey and almonds and pistachio nuts and dates, and good wheat flour and leaven. And I'm sure there's enough for all."

The boy in her arms struggled to get away from her, but not convincingly. "You ain't my mother," he said. "You don't like me."

"I love you," Mary said, and the way her eyes shone made the child wriggle in embarrassment. Mary looked at the others in the group, and those in the smaller crowd who had dropped their sticks and stones.

Never, Joseph thought, had he seen bigger eyes than those revealed by the torchlight and the lamp glow and the star shine, and in the brightness and glare of the oven fire.

A tall girl, Judith, thin and ugly, shook her mane of dingy red hair in pretended scorn and anger.

"Maybe you can love a little boy," she said. "But someone like me? Oh no! Nobody loves a thing like me!"

Mary held open her arms to the girl. The boy reeled away from her, as though he were dizzy with happiness, and the girl jumped — actually jumped — into them. Mary held her, and let her cry until she finished. "I love you," Mary answered her. "And God loves you. God is coming down to earth, because he loves you; because he loves all little children; because he loves everybody, even the worst of sinners!"

The grocer and the baker worked diligently, even while they kept looking at Mary and the children. They wrapped many loaves of bread. They wrapped many pieces of cheese. They wrapped mangoes and dates and figs and oranges and combs of honey. When everything was wrapped Nathan raised his voice.

"Michael! Daniel! Moses!"

Three young men came running from somewhere in the rear of the bakery, armed with long heavy sticks. "Light torches," Nathan bade them. "And take the lady and her husband to the caves."

"We'll have a banquet there," Joseph told the children.

Some of them began to dance and to shout for joy. They were so noisy that a number of Roman soldiers, on foot, hurried to the marketplace to see who was being killed. And the stars began to assemble in heaven that they might witness all the things that would happen in Bethlehem that night.

"We'll clean the place," the tall girl said. She was sniffling and laughing at the same time. Her eyes were shining. They kept filling with tears, no matter how hard she bit her lips, nor how tough she made her voice. And she couldn't help trying to arrange her hair and her dress, any more than she could help trying to make sure, with her rain-washed hands, that her face was not too dirty. "Everybody get water," she said. "And everybody get brooms. Don't stand there. The rain has stopped. Move!"

Two of the bigger boys caught fire from the girl. "You fellows get wood," one shouted. "Anything that will burn. Bring it to the cave. And get straw, clean straw."

"The rest of you," yelled the other boy, "get shovels. And buckets. And water too. We'll clean the stable."

Little boys and girls sped through the starry darkness. Others formed a sort of honor guard around Mary, who was again enthroned in the saddle. The boys with the torches went ahead, like acolytes. The big boys and girls carried some of the wrapped packages. Joseph carried a few. Nathan carried a loaf of bread in each hand. Only the baker was left behind. Someone had to stay.

At sight of the grocer Joseph looked guilty.

"I forgot to pay you, Nathan of Bethlehem," he said. He reached for his his purse, but Nathan shook his head warningly from side to side.

"God's blessing on your house," he said. "I am glad I had something to give in God's most blessed name. But — but don't you tell anybody it was a gift. And you children — if you talk, I'll set the boys on you next time you come. You hear Michael? You hear, Daniel? You hear, Moses? And you will bring gifts too. You hear?"

"I got a gift," one of the boys cried, from out of the darkness somewhere beyond the donkey. "I got a Roman coin."

"You stole it," another voice said. "You want to get the Baby locked up because of a dirty old stolen Roman coin? I got something good. I got a golden bird. He's got a broken leg, but he can sing!"

"I have a flower," a girl cried. "Would the Baby like a flower?"

Joseph wondered at all this. Nobody had said Mary's Child

was the Messiah so long awaited. Yet everybody seemed to sense it.

He began to sing again: "The rivers shall clap their hands, the mountains rejoice together at the presence of the Lord; because he cometh to judge the earth." Mary jingled the bells as he sang.

The children made him sing it again and again; and they clapped their hands as they sang.

"Behold thy Savior cometh," Joseph sang; and this time they let him sing alone, enchanted by the richness of his voice, the splendor of the words, the glory of the night. It was cold. The wind had died. The sky had dropped so low that everyone could see that the stars were heavily frosted. "Behold his reward is with him, and his work before him. . . . All the nations thou hast made shall come and adore before thee, O Lord; and they shall glorify thy name. The Kings of Tharsis and the islands shall offer presents; the kings of the Arabians and Saba shall bring gifts."

"Everybody bring gifts," the tall girl ordered. She was under full control again, she thought; and she had more power than she knew what to do with. She cried out, in a voice loud enough and shrill enough to reach all the little ones running for brooms or water, "Everybody bring a present to the Baby!"

No king, returning in victory, with captives and spoils, ever brought such true joy with him, Joseph thought. None ever made his people half so happy. And no man, king or commoner, had ever traveled with so beautiful and generous and compassionate a queen!

Nathan said good night to Joseph at the entrance to the cave, and he bowed low to Mary.

"I was reading of another Joseph when you came," he said, "the Joseph who was lord of Egypt. Pharaoh called him 'the savior of the world.' When the people cried for food, he bade them 'Go to Joseph.' I have seen the hungry go to Joseph — and to his noble wife. I have been blessed. And I am happy for the first time since my wife, Miriam, went to the bosom of our father, Abraham. May the child be a son — and another saintly Joseph!"

The grotto was just such a place as Joseph's house, or Mary's, but it had more chambers, it was deeper in the earth, and the ceilings were much higher. There was a stable, separated by a few boards, from the largest chamber. Joseph tethered the donkey there, after relieving him of his bulging saddlebags, his harness, and the string of silver bells.

"We'll clean up first," the tall girl shouted. "Then we'll eat."

The torches were placed where they could best light the room. Oil lamps were lit and placed on a wide ledge above the floor. And the little thieves went swiftly (and inexpertly) to work. Joseph took care of the donkey. Mary summoned the littlest boy to her, the one she had hugged.

"Here I am," she said, "all alone, with nobody to help me unwrap the food."

The boy rushed to her. "Let me!" he said. "Let me." He looked helplessly into her face. "You're pretty," he said. "Did you mean it when you said — when you said . . .?"

"Oh, very much," Mary answered, handing him a loaf to unwrap. "I love you more than you'll ever know."

He held his head down and wept quietly, but his fingers tore off the paper hurriedly and reached for another loaf. "Does he love me too?" he asked, pointing at Joseph.

"He thinks you smell of heaven," Mary told him.

"I like his smell too," the boy answered, beginning to smile. "Donkeys. Sweat. Wood. And soap. Do you like soap?"

"Go to Joseph," Mary said. "He may have a piece."

"I got an ox," the boy said, "for your Baby."

"An ox?"

The tall girl overheard him. She settled herself confidentially at Mary's knee, and helped her prepare the feast. "He and his brothers and sisters haven't any fire in their house," she explained. "It is cold in the morning, too cold to dress. They snatch up their things and run naked into the stable. The ox is there. He is always warm. So warm! They snuggle up to him and dress. Isaac thinks your Baby will want to snuggle up to the ox tomorrow."

"And I'm an artist," the boy said. "I'll draw him a sheep when I come back tomorrow. I can draw a sheep good. A great big sheep too. And I'm going to draw you too. You're so pretty!"

"Shut up," the girl snapped. "Shut up and work."

Tears threatened her again. She shook them angrily away.

Mary smiled at her. "Suppose you ring those little bells," she suggested. "You must be starved."

The girl forgot her tears. She jumped up, singing: "The rivers shall clap their hands." She rang the bells long and joyously; the first Christmas bells ever to ring on earth.

After the children had devoured everything except a crust of bread — and some of them fell asleep while eating — they said the politest good nights they knew, and scampered out of the cave. Then one little boy came running back. He rushed up to Mary, and into her arms.

"I love you too," he said. "Oh, I do love you too!"

Someone was chasing him. It was the tall girl. "Come on now, you imp," she said roughly. "The lady is tired, and she's going to have a baby, and she wants to be alone." But she couldn't go through with the act. She fell, weeping again, and covered Mary's hands with hot wet kisses. "I love you too." She grabbed up the boy and hurried with him, under her right arm, into the night.

Joseph put out the torches and all but two of the lamps. He took two cups from one of the saddlebags and poured some wine into them. One cup was half full, his own. The other held a few drops. He gave that to Mary, and handed her the surviving crust of bread. He sat across the fire from her, worrying again. She was wearing bright colors. Her hair was unbound, fine, beautiful, long, thick, a glossy ripple of glory. It framed her head like a halo; and the capering flames of the wood fire made the halo dance. She was kneeling, looking up toward the ceiling. "I have loved, O Lord, the beauty of thy house," she said, "and the place where thy glory dwelleth. This is your house, for here you will bring forth your Son." She ate a little of the bread and sipped the wine. She looked at her husband.

"And blessed are you, Joseph, among all men. The Child within me leaps for joy every time you venture near me. You shall be the seeing eye of all the prophets, the listening ear, the ministering hand. You shall see the fulfillment of their dreams!"

Joseph didn't understand her calmness, her strange lack of fear. Was she all right? She had told him not to worry, but he couldn't help worrying. She had said she would not need a midwife. But suppose she did need one, and needed her desperately?

"The holy ones of Israel spoke of him," Mary said, "and sang of him, and dreamed of him, and longed to see him, to hear every word he might utter. They died hungering and thirsting for him. But you, my Joseph, will see him every day. You will hear his baby talk by day and his cries by night. You will hold him and sing him to sleep. You will sing hymns to him, and he will sing to you. You will for him, and he for you. You will teach him many things. You will make a man of him.

"Was any other man so blessed that he should be chosen to make a man of the Almighty?"

Joseph bowed his head, unable to bear the glory of her face, nor the wonder of her words.

"Now line the manger with clean straw, my prince," she begged him. "I shall place the Baby there, where the ox and the ass are fed — for the Child is coming soon to feed himself to the hungry world."

CHAPTER VIII

Joseph rested, after he had put the straw in the manger. He leaned back against the wooden side of the stable and went to sleep. He hadn't meant to sleep, but he had walked nearly thirty miles that day, and had eaten little. The breath of the ox, warming his neck, awakened him. He turned and looked at the animal. He remembered the little boy who had promised to bring him. He smiled and turned around to see how Mary was. He sprang up, suddenly pierced with shame. How could he have slept?

She was standing before the ledge on which the two lamps burned; a ledge that God had made out of the limestone uncounted thousands of years ago, a ledge that looked like an altar. She was standing erect; like a priest about to sacrifice a lamb, Joseph thought, and she was praying aloud.

"The Lord hath said to me; Thou art my Son, this day have I begotten thee. . . . Send forth thy light and thy truth; they have conducted me and brought me unto thy holy hill and into thy tabernacles."

She sank slowly to her knees, and Joseph, somewhat reassured about her, put the last of the wood on the fire.

He heard Mary laughing. He was standing close to the fire, yet he felt he had turned to ice! But there was something so merry in her laughter, and such a great surprise, that he began to thaw.

Nobody had ever laughed with such genuine amusement and love in all the history of the world. And nobody would ever laugh like that again!

The Baby had been born! He lay in the straw, in front of his kneeling mother. He was as rosy and clean as though he had been bathed and powdered. And he was beautiful and strong!

"To play such a trick on your poor mother," Mary said to him. "It was a wonderful trick! But how could I expect it? A moment ago I felt you moving in my womb. Now you lie there looking at me with your eyes of God!"

A great many years later, St. John the Evangelist wrote of the time Jesus came into a room without any effort, though all the windows and doors were locked. It was after his resurrection and his disciples were gathered together. Jesus appeared in the midst of them, saying "Peace be to You." He vanished in the same mysterious, stupefying way.

At first Joseph paid more attention to Mary than to the Child. She was as slim as she had been when he first saw her! She was well! She was infinitely more beautiful. Evidently she had felt no pain, needed no help! He could not understand what had happened. He would never fully understand — nor would anybody else.

He knew his virgin wife had given birth, yet still remained a virgin. God had come out of her womb as simply as he had entered it. He had delivered himself, through his own power! He did not cry when he came into the world. He made no sound at all!

Joseph watched, motionless, as Mary played with the Baby and adored Him. He saw her touch the perfect little hands. He saw her caress them. He saw her feel the perfect shoulders and draw her fingertips down his perfect sides. He watched her as she played with the round little belly.

And only then did the blood surge back into his body from

wherever it had fled. He knelt beside his wife and looked at her and the Infant she held against her bosom.

This was God! This was the Almighty, the Terrible! And yet this was also a Baby. Helpless, soft, dependent on his mother. . . . "And on me too," thought Joseph. "On me, a sinner!"

The voice of Isaias spoke through Joseph: "For a Child is born to us, and a son is given to us, and the government is upon his shoulder; and his name shall be called Wonderful, Counsellor, God the Mighty, the Father of the world to come, the Prince of Peace. His empire shall be multiplied, and there shall be no end of peace; he shall sit upon the throne of David."

Mary, too excited and too steeped in adoration to speak, motioned for the swaddling clothes she had placed near the manger. Joseph gave them to her, his hands trembling. Mary covered the Baby deftly and swiftly, stood up, and placed him in the manger.

Joseph knelt, and the tears that always welled up in him when he saw beauty, made a sort of rainbow between him and the Child. He spoke with the voice of Job:

"For I know that my Redeemer liveth. . . ."

But he brought Job up to date. "Aye, I know that my Redeemer liveth, and here and now, in my own flesh, I look at God; whom I myself see with my own eyes. I see my God, and yet I do not die!"

He was silent. Mary, kneeling on the other side of the manger, was also silent. Angels were singing in the frosty sky, but Mary and Joseph had a more glorious music than the angels' song. They were listening to the soft and even and gentle breathing of the Baby, Jesus.

Men with lanterns and torches stole into the cave, walking as quietly as possible in their clumsy boots. Mary rose to receive and welcome them as though they were her children coming home late from a party.

They were shepherds, they said, and had come to see and adore the Baby.

"We saw angels," one said. "And we heard them. They were singing. You wouldn't believe how they sang. They sent us here."

They must have run most of the way, Mary thought. Every one of them was panting.

"We were frightened," a young shepherd said. "We were watching our flocks not far from here. I saw an angel. One angel at first. I saw him because, all of a sudden, the dark night had become lighter than day. The angel saw we were all scared. He told us not to be afraid. He had good tidings, he said. Tidings of great joy. He wanted everybody to share that joy. He said:

" 'For this day is born to you a Savior, who is Christ, the Lord, in the city of David. And this shall be a sign unto you; you shall find the infant wrapped in swaddling clothes, and laid in a manger.'

"That's exactly what he said. And then there were millions and millions of other angels. And they were singing loud enough to wake everybody in all Israel. And they sang: 'Glory to God in the highest; and on earth peace to men of goodwill!' We dropped everything, and ran. We even left the sheep!"

"Here is the Child," Mary said. She had been standing in front of the manger and her kneeling husband. Now she stepped aside. Instantly all the shepherds, including those still struggling with their sheepskin coats, fell on their knees in silent adoration.

She could almost see these men as they hurried through the flinty fields and up the rocky hills, heading directly toward the cave. They were the least regarded of the Jews, these shepherds. And the Jews were the least regarded in all the "iron curtain" portions of the Roman world. So God had sent his angels to invite them. They were the very first guests invited to witness this miracle of Divine Love!

"The courtesy of God!" she thought. "One angel would not

do to summon these humble men, the humblest in his kingdom. No. God must send 'millions and millions' of angels. Choirs and choirs.

"How happy God must be — to see his Son lying in this humble place, surrounded by these poor and lowly men! How different are his standards from those of his proud creatures!"

She reached down into the straw in the manger, lifted the Baby carefully, held him to her breast, and turned his face toward them.

"A lamb!" one said.

"A king," said another. "Our King! The Christ!"

"The Savior," said a third. "The Savior who is Christ the Lord!"

"Glory to God in the highest," said a fourth. "That's what the angels said. God! The Baby is God! They came down like falling stars, but brighter. Singing! Singing 'Glory to God!' "

Joseph, who had risen from his knees when Mary lifted Jesus in her arms, looked at the shepherds with the eyes of one awakened from a wondrous dream.

"Aye," he said. "He is a King. He is the Christ. Behold the King of heaven and earth. The King of angels. The King of sinners. Behold God made flesh, the Almighty born of a woman! Glory indeed to God, and peace to men of goodwill."

Mary placed the Child in Joseph's arms; and Joseph was so flustered, and so filled with emotion, he almost dropped him.

The Baby opened his eyes as he was lowered to his straw-stuffed throne, and Joseph looked as deeply into them as he had once looked into the eyes of Mary.

He was lost again to everything around him. He did not see the Shepherds go. He did not see the children scamper in.

The sound of someone weeping brought him back to time and space, and to an awareness of people about him. He saw that it was the tall girl, Judith, who wept.

"Child," he said softly, "this is the happiest day God ever made. Nobody should cry on such a happy day."

The girl looked at him with humor and scorn, and another burst of tears. "What else can you do when you're so happy you could die? Smile like a ninny? Last night I was so cold and hungry, and so sick of everything, I wanted to kill myself. Now I want to live a thousand years. I keep looking at him and I keeping crying. I can't help it. It's like he wasn't your Baby at all, or hers, but mine. All mine! Wouldn't you cry, if you were an ugly girl and you had a Baby like that?"

"God bless you," Joseph said. "Cry all you want. The Most High will pay back every tear of love."

He smiled at the girl and she stopped crying. His gaze returned to the manger. "Aye," he said, "I gave up all hope of fatherhood. And what other father was ever given such a Child as this?"

He rose and went to join Mary and the children who surrounded her. She was telling them the story of Adam and Eve, their first parents, of their exile from paradise, and of God's promise of a Redeemer.

CHAPTER IX

The glad tidings brought by the angels were spread through the countryside by the shepherds and the children; and for weeks people from near and far came to see the Baby, and to bring him gifts. Joseph moved his family into a house in the town. Nathan helped him find the place, and the children helped him clean it. Nathan secured work for him at the inn, and Joseph decided to remain in Bethlehem. There was only one regret. He had not brought the cradle with him.

On the eighth day Jesus was circumcized, as the law of Moses commanded, and the house was filled all day and well into the night with friendly people.

On the fortieth day, early in the morning, Jesus was taken to Jerusalem to be presented to his Father. It was the law that every firstborn son should be "consecrated to the Lord"; but, for five shekels, he could be ransomed — freed from all obligations to serve the priests in the Temple. It was the law that every woman should be "purified" forty days after the birth of a son. One could become unclean in many ways under the Mosaic law as interpreted by the Scribes and Pharisees. A woman bearing a child was unclean, and everyone she touched during her pregnancy was unclean. She must make a "sin offering" — anything from a yearling lamb to a pair of turtledoves. Then she and her baby would be cleansed. The baby, of course, had become "unclean" because of his "unclean" mother. But the lamb, or the doves, would serve to free him, as well as the mother, from all levitical contamination.

Joseph had spent much time grooming the donkey for this solemn occasion, but, at the last minute, he decided not to string the bells around the saddle. The priests might think it disrespectful if the beast came to the Temple walking to such gay music.

A crowd of children ran with the Holy Family a little way, bidding them good-bye; and they stood a long time in the road, waiting until the travelers had disappeared over the first hill.

"This," Mary confided to Joseph, "is even a happier day than the day he was conceived or the day he was born. Today he visits the house of his Father! Today he will be formally introduced to his Father! Today he will be given to his Father! And where the Father and the Son meet, there also is the Holy Ghost!"

Joseph remembered part of the verse of Malachy that Mary had quoted in the home of Zachary. He sang it:

"The Lord whom you seek, and the angel of the testament whom you desire, shall come to his temple. Behold he cometh, saith the Lord of hosts."

And he sang some verses from Isaias:

"Behold my servant, I will uphold him; my elect, my soul delighteth in him; I have given my spirit upon him, he shall bring forth judgment to the Gentiles. . . . The bruised reed he shall not break, and smoking flax he shall not quench. . . . I, the Lord, have called thee in justice, and taken thee by the hand, and preserved thee. And I have given thee for a covenant of the people, for a light to the gentiles. . . . Behold, I have given thee to the light of the gentiles, that thou mayest be my salvation even to the farthest part of the earth."

He gave Mary an odd look. "The gentiles," he said. "I must

have been thinking of Cyrus the Persian who gave me the bells for my firstborn, or for the little Messiah."

"He comes not only to Israel," Mary said, "but to all the gentile world as well."

They stopped when they saw the Temple, the gold and marble structure built to express the people's love and reverence for their God. They rested awhile; and Joseph made sure that Mary and Jesus were not too cold. Then Joseph spoke to the donkey, leading him on again. And again he sang:

"I rejoiced at the things that were said to me; we shall go into the house of the Lord."

And he cried out in an exultant voice: "Lift up your gates, O Jerusalem, and the King of Glory shall enter in. . . ."

Their rapture waned as they approached the Temple gates, for they were beset, accosted, and surrounded by a multitude of shouting buyers and sellers of cattle and sheep and doves. The voices of these men competed with the noises of the animals and birds. They spoke in a babel of tongues. They made odd gestures, threatening, angry, greedy, beguiling gestures. And there was a more nauseating smell about them than about the creatures in which they dealt.

After coming from a long spiritual retreat, and intimate communion with the Lord, Mary and Joseph found themselves in a whirlpool of devilish clamor, vulgarity, and stench!

Instinctively Mary turned the Child's face toward her, that he might not see the evil faces of the men around him; and she tightened her arms a trifle, as Joseph stopped to buy two doves.

Inside the courtyard hundreds of levites, on the gleaming white steps, were singing the praises of the Lord. Scores of priests were washing their hands in the great basin upheld by the backs of a dozen golden oxen. Guards were pacing everywhere, looking at everyone with suspicion and distrust. There was prayer here, Mary acknowledged, but it was mechanical,

not born of affection. It was as much a part of the routine as the
cheating of the money changers, the haggling of the dealers, the
rudeness of the guards.

An old man and a very old woman saw Mary and Joseph
standing at the foot of the steps, straight as two candles burning
before the Lord. The man, Simeon, who had longed most of his
life to look upon the Consolation of Israel, saw the Child Mary
held. He went through the crowds directly toward her, the
woman following him.

The Holy Ghost was in Simeon. The Holy Ghost had led him
into the Temple this day. The Holy Ghost had promised he
should not die until he had seen the Christ. And the Spirit of
God was in the woman, Anna, also. She had spent more than
fifty years, since she was widowed, serving in the Temple day
and night, never leaving the place, praying constantly and fasting
often.

Flame leaps to flame. Mary recognized true love in Simeon's
face. She moved toward him, and placed her Son in his outstretched arms.

"Now thou dost dismiss thy servant, Lord," the old man said,
speaking to the sleeping Baby, "according to thy word, in peace;
because mine eyes have seen thy salvation, which thou hast
prepared before the face of all peoples; a light of revelation to
the gentiles, and the glory of thy people, Israel."

Simeon, Joseph thought, looked like Zachary. But his face
was shining! Zachary had seen an angel. Simeon was looking
at the Christ.

There was something of the same glory, Joseph decided, in the
face of the Prophetess Anna. Yet it was plain she felt herself
unworthy to hold the Lord of life and death, the Savior of the
world. It was enough, and more than enough, just to look at him.

"Both are eager to die," he thought, "now that their prayers
have been heard. God has given them his choicest wine to drink.

Each will break the chalice gladly, that it may never hold a lesser vintage."

Simeon gave the Baby reluctantly back to Mary; and there was a shadow of sadness on his beaming face.

"Behold," he said, "this Child is set for the fall and the resurrection of many in Israel, and for a sign that shall be contradicted. And thine own soul a sword shall pierce, that out of many hearts thoughts may be revealed."

A sword! There was only one sword that could ever frighten Mary, or cause her anxiety or anguish. It was a sword shaped like a cross, and it was in the hand of Abraham as he bent above his much loved Isaac, ready to sacrifice him to the Lord. It was here on Mount Moriah, where the Temple rose in glory, that Abraham had built his altar and placed his son upon it as a holocaust. It might have been exactly here, at the foot of these steps.

Isaac had carried the wood up the slope of the mountain. He had carried it on his back. Abraham had followed, sword in one hand, torch in the other, calm speech on his lips, misery in his heart. Isaac must have wondered why his father placed the wood on the altar before obtaining a victim to place upon the wood. How did he feel when he realized the victim was himself?

The sword had dropped from the hand of Abraham into the heart of the virgin mother; and it had slashed away the joyous gauze with which she had covered her knowledge of the sacrifice she must some day make. Now the texts she had hidden from herself were revealed in all their terror:

"He shall be led as a sheep to the slaughter. . . . For the wickedness of my people have I struck him. . . . They have pierced my hands and my feet, they have numbered all my bones."

Scourges would number all the bones of her Son, Jesus. He would be forced to carry the wood up the slope. He would be nailed to it with great iron spikes. It was a Roman world. It would be a Roman death. A cross would rise on a rocky hill, its splintered arms reaching out to embrace the world; and the Victim would die upon it. God had provided a ram as a substitute for Isaac. But he would not spare Jesus. He would sacrifice His much loved Son for the children of Abraham, the children of Isaac and Ishmael, for all men, gentiles and Jews.

Joseph, who had been startled by hearing Simeon's prophecy of a sword, looked quickly at his wife; but saw no sign of fear in her, nor the least indication of grief or pain or suffering of any kind. He saw only rapture in her face; and that was natural, for the living God was in her arms.

In the hush that followed the departure of Simeon and Anna, Mary heard the bleating of a lamb. She drew her own Lamb closer to her. She caressed his silky hair, and fondled his hands and feet. "I am your handmaid," she told him silently, "as well as your adoring mother. Your holy will be done."

She walked with Joseph, easily, valiantly, into the Temple, into the presence of busy priests who scarcely looked at her or her husband or her Baby. The doves were given, received, and slain. The sinless virgin was levitically made clean. The Child was presented to his Father — and to the Holy Ghost, and consecrated according to the law of Moses. And, by Mary, he was offered as a willing holocaust. Isaac may have wept and struggled when he realized what his father meant to do. Jesus could not be ignorant of his Father's will; and he would not struggle, he would not rebel.

The shekels were paid — a shekel for each of the frightful wounds the Christ would suffer to expiate the sins of men. And the priests hurried off to other routine tasks.

"I should be happy," Joseph said as he led the donkey homeward. "But somehow I'm not. I'm glad I left the bells at home. And I do not feel at all like singing."

CHAPTER X

About the time that Mary and Joseph returned to Bethlehem, a caravan far to the east got under way, its dromedaries swaggering and swaying across the round yellow face of the rising moon. This procession moved only in the night. It was led by three wise men, three Magi, three astronomers. Their names have come down to us as Melchior, Gaspar, and Balthasar.

These men, descendants of Chaldeans, Medes, and Persians, believed implicitly in the oneness of God. They had been influenced by the Prophet Daniel, who had been honored by Chaldean and Persian kings because he loved and honored his God, the God of the Jews. They had also learned something from the Prophet Balaam, who was, like themselves, a descendant of Ishmael.

They knew it was time for the birth of the Savior, predicted by so many of the Hebrew prophets. They knew his coming would be announced by a star; for Balaam had written: "A star shall rise out of Jacob and a scepter shall spring up from Israel." They knew, by this, that the Savior would be the King of heaven and earth. It was necessary, they felt, to seek him out, to bring him rich presents, to adore him, and to pledge him loyalty.

His star had appeared in the western sky shortly after Melchior's son, Cyrus, had returned with the glorious news that the

Saint of saints was in the womb. It was such a star as none of
the wise men had even seen before. It was a great blazing fire,
so bright it gave a shadow to every man and beast that moved
in the night. It was a summons and a proclamation. It told the
men of the East that earth had reached its happiest morning,
its happiest hour; and it bade them come and adore the
long-awaited Savior-King — God's most precious Gift to all his
children.

The star seemed to have an unnatural, brightening intelligence.
It went before the caravan steadily through the night. It halted
when the riders halted. It slept when the men and animals slept.
It woke for duty when the sun fell, and the men could come out
of their tents, and the cooks could prepare the food.

When the animals had been given food and drink, and the
tents had been folded and packed, and the fires had been smoth-
ered, the star resumed command.

Lucifer, prince of darkness and lord of the night, brooded
and fumed as the caravan came nearer and nearer to the rocks
of Palestine.

He hated the star because it was like the beckoning finger of
God, whom he hated with an eternal hate. He hated the men
of the caravan because they came in the name of God, singing
his praises, and because they meant to adore the Infant born
in the stable in that wretched Bethlehem. Lucifer suspected the
Child might be the Redeemer the Most High had promised.
But he wasn't sure. The Messiah, he knew, would be born of
a virgin. He had always felt that Mary was the virgin God had
chosen. He felt this because he had such an intense hatred of
her, and such an unreasonable fear. Was she the one who would
crush his head, the one for whose heel he must lie in wait?
Perhaps he had been mistaken about her. She had married a
young man. How then could she remain a virgin? Forty days
after her Child was born, she had gone to the Temple to be

purified. Also, she had made a sin offering! This was strange indeed, for Satan could remember no sin she had committed. So far as he knew she had not even the taint of original sin. She baffled him. She infuriated him. She left him helpless.

He had almost convinced himself that Jesus was not the Son of God. Yet facts made all his angelic logic stagger. Those angels singing to the shepherds! One had said something about a Savior wrapped in swaddling clothes and laid in a manger. But would the Almighty permit His Son to be born in a common stable? Lucifer hadn't heard all the message these angels brought; for they came in such a volume of light that he was outraged. He fled from them. Light — any light — was an affront to him.

He could not explain the angels. He could not explain the joy in Simeon's face as he held the Baby in the Temple; nor the old man's eagerness to be dismissed from life now that he had seen "the light to the revelation of the gentiles and the glory of thy people Israel." He would have gone closer to Simeon except for Mary. He was among friends in the Temple. He had felt at home, until he saw her there.

And the happiness of that old prophetess, Anna! She hadn't smiled like that in fifty years! She angered and puzzled him too. So did the adoring shepherds and the children.

And now these men from the East, with the long shadows crawling behind them! They came like holy pilgrims fleeing a land of shadows, seeking a newborn Light!

He listened to the babble of the Magi and their retinue. And he began to swell with wrath and pride and jealousy. These men thought the Infant was not only God, but the king of the earth as well. Let him be God, if he must, Lucifer thought; but he would never be king of the earth. He would never wrest the earth from the emperor of hell. Never!

The Child must be killed, Lucifer decided. Why not let him be killed by the Magi who had come so far, and so piously, to adore him? If he had a sense of irony he would have laughed, if he could laugh. "Aye, they shall kill the Son of God, or the Prophet — whichever he may be. They shall kill him through my dear friend, Herod! I will lead the Persians to King Herod. When he learns that the Child they seek is to be the king of the Jews — the king of the world — my gifted murderer will go right willingly to work. I can leave the details to him. He can reach the Child. I can't, so long as his mother guards him. Suppose she were to see him killed! What a delightful thought! I shall arrange it, I shall forge the sword in hell, and put a delightfully sharp edge on it. The Magi will bring it to the royal court. Herod will use it. And I shall continue to reign upon the earth."

He waited impatiently for the caravan. When it neared Jerusalem, he had grown so tall in stature, through his fury and his pride, his somber wings had no trouble in blotting out the guiding star.

The Magi, lost, began to ask the people of Jerusalem, "Where is he that is born king of the Jews?" The people wakened Herod. Herod called in the chief priests and scribes and questioned them. They looked at the Scripture and discovered that indeed a king was to be born to the world. In Bethlehem, the city of David. Herod veiled his emotions with the slyest of smiles, and admitted the wise men to his room.

"You will find the little one in Bethlehem," he said. "When you find him, bring me word, so I too may go and worship him. Now tell me all about the star — especially when you first saw it."

The wise men backed ceremoniously out of the royal presence and returned to the caravan. And, lo, the star appeared again. It led them into the city of David. It hovered over the roof of the humblest dwelling in the town. The Child was with his mother. A green shoot of a girl with her first Blossom in her arms. A gracious queen. She was not in the least impressed with their wealth or rank or importance. She welcomed them like a mother. It was they who were impressed and awed. And the Child? He was so regal and beautiful and resplendent they could not help falling down, like slaves before their master, and adoring him.

"A light to the revelation of the gentiles," Mary repeated Simeon's words to herself. "First the humble shepherds were invited to kneel before him. Now these wise men, these gentiles, these aristocrats of the intellect, these men of place and power, are ushered to his throne by a star!"

Servants brought in bags of treasure. Gold. Frankincense. Myrrh. Gold for a king. Frankincense for God. Myrrh for a mortal man. The servants, and all the others in the caravan, prostrated themselves and asked a blessing on themselves and their children and their children's children. And they left the lowly home with more ceremony than they had shown in Herod's palace.

Joseph returned home late. He asked if Cyrus had come with the others. He described him. Mary said he had not come. Joseph was disappointed. Perhaps, though, a man with triplets should stay home with them.

Mary was sorry Joseph had not been at home to welcome the strangers. They had come so far. It had taken them months. They came to spend only a few moments, then to return! Surely those gentiles loved God very much! Joseph must see them tomorrow.

But when morning came, she and Joseph and the Baby were miles away from Bethlehem. For, shortly after Joseph had gone to sleep, an angel came to him in a dream, and warned him Herod was looking for Jesus, meaning to destroy him. "Take the Child and his mother," the angel commanded, "and go into Egypt. Stay there until I tell you to come back."

Mary, asking no questions, helped Joseph prepare for flight. They snatched up only what was essential. Water. Bread. Wine. Olives. A few heavy wraps. Some lengths of cloth that could be fashioned into a tent. The gifts of the Magi. Joseph's kit of tools. The bells, which would attract attention, Joseph secured in one of the packs. Mary loved those bells. She often amused the Baby with them. The Baby loved them too. The bells must go along.

The streets of Bethlehem seemed to be deserted. The donkey went at his natural gait until he descended into the valley below the town. Then Joseph made him quicken his pace. They had but one fear — Herod. Toward morning they found a rough sort of refuge, a cleft in a rocky ledge, where Joseph made a sort of tent. They remained under cover all day.

Mary seldom let the Child out of her arms during the entire journey. She could not otherwise have borne her sorrow. Again and again she thought of Simeon. Her Child indeed had been set for the fall and the resurrection of many in Israel, and for a sign that should be contradicted. Just yesterday he was openly God and King. Today an earthbound king was hunting him. He must walk in the darkness, and hide in the light. Yesterday all the people of Bethlehem had loved and adored him. He had been forced to leave them, abruptly, rudely. They would weep for him. They would think themselves abandoned!

The way was rough, the weather hot by day, cold by night. God did not provide a star for these fugitives, nor did he furnish the sky-soaring pillar of fire and the earth-walking cloud he had given the children of Israel when they fled, with Moses, out of Egypt. He did not send down manna in the wilderness, nor supply them with sweet water gushing out of dusty rocks.

God had a purpose in letting his best loved children suffer hardships and perils. Millions and millions of outlawed, displaced, persecuted, and hunted people have seen something of that purpose, and drawn some measure of comfort from the knowledge that "The Lord is one of us!"

There were many Jews in Egypt. They helped the Holy Family find shelter, and Joseph to obtain work. The fatigue of the long march was forgotten, the fear, the sunburn, the cold, the winds, the hunger and thirst, the tension of being constantly on the alert. Joseph felt safe in Egypt; for, since it was the devil's country, the devil and all his cohorts would never look for Jesus here. One had only to look at the Egyptian gods to know who ruled the land. Lucifer had made gods of the basest of animals, to mock the living God — vultures, jackals, mad dogs, serpents, and fearful bulls. Aye, there was safety here, and sights to see.

There were times when Mary felt so relaxed she could let her Baby sleep in the shade, or play with the children of the neighborhood, gentiles and Jews, while she washed the linen, or prepared the vegetables for dinner, or listened to the heartache of some other woman.

There were times when Mary and Joseph had nothing to do but walk around and look at the world that God had made. On these occasions Joseph carried Jesus on his shoulder; and Mary walked at his side. Joseph, who had learned much about Egypt and its customs from the men with whom he worked, was always the guide and lecturer. Man-made things in this strange country also fascinated him. He delighted in showing and explaining them to Mary and the Child.

"This is the Sphinx. It is thousands of years old. The powerful body of a beast, the face of a benevolent, intelligent, dignified man. It is a symbol of body and soul. It indicates the mixture of good and bad in a man. The noblest and wisest of men are animals; and the beast will prevail at times. The worst and most ignorant of men are still men, for all the brute in them.

And now and then the angel in them will tame and control what is animal. People speak of the riddle of the Sphinx. There is as great a riddle in a man."

He gestured toward the pyramids, lavender and gray against a gray-blue sky.

"There we see the human desire for immortality, for godhood! Man wants to make something and be something that will never die. The mummies of kings are entombed there — men who believed they could attain eternal life, eternal majesty, eternal power, and eternal splendor, inside eternal mounds of stone.

They studied the three piles of well-cut, well-placed rocks, the product of sweat and tears and toil of uncounted thousands of slaves. And they saw the symbol of the Trinity: Father, Son, and Holy Ghost!

They looked at the copper-colored Nile that had stained its valley green, at the sun boats on its bosom, at the squalor and bustle and clamor of the markets near its banks. They gazed at the beauty of the temples, at the artistry spent on the making of the many gods, at the numerous little mud-brick houses. They looked at the people, as poor and as wretched and as helpless as the people of Israel, and pitied them and prayed for them — and helped them with the gold of the Magi.

From another fugitive they learned of the massacre of the innocents. The Magi had not gone back to Herod. The angel who had warned Joseph of the plot against the Child, had warned the wise men also. They went home by a route that bypassed Jerusalem. Herod, made doubly furious by this public snub, and by his failure to learn the identity of the one who had dared to be his rival, ordered the massacre of all the baby boys, in and around Bethlehem, who were two years old or younger.

The soldiers used Herod's own unholy guile. They made it known through all the region that the great king Herod, in order to honor his own son, was eager to prefer royal honors on all male children born in and near the City of David within the past two years. Mothers were instructed to bring their sons to a certain place at a certain hour on a certain day, that they might receive the royal recognition.

One soldier told the women their children would become blood kin to Herod's son, the storyteller said. This induced some women to cheat. They came with babies more than two years old, thinking, "what soldier can tell a baby's age?"

One by one the women were ushered out of the waiting room, up several flights of stairs, down a corridor, into a room where a soldier waited, bloodstained sword in hand. The child was swiftly wrenched from his mother's arms, was neatly and quickly stabbed, and was then thrown through the window onto the stone-flagged court below. If the mother screamed it did not matter. Those waiting the king's blessing would not hear her.

At that, the storyteller added, the children did become blood kin of Herod's son; for the king cut his son's head off a day or two after the massacre — a pleasure he had long denied himself.

Though she was far away in time and space, Mary could hear the women weeping and wailing. She prayed that their empty hearts might fill with resignation, with peace, and with new love. She had known two of those women, the mothers of Judith and of little Isaac; and she had loved them.

She knew that some were bitter and that they blamed her and Joseph for the tragedy. She could hear them talking: "Those two killed my boy! They knew what Herod was going to do. They must have known. Otherwise they would not have fled. They could have warned me. But they didn't. They didn't care about my son. They saved their own at my boy's expense. They killed him! God forgive them!"

She took Jesus for a walk. "Let them understand that their children are the first saints in your kingdom of sinners," she prayed to him. "Let them know they too may become saints. For, even though they hated and despised me and Joseph, and wanted to get even with us, they protected you. It would have been easy to mention your name to the soldiers and point to the hoof prints of the donkey. The soldiers could have found us. They would have slain you. With what awful joy they would have reported your murder to their king! Those women did not betray you, Jesus. They still love and adore you. Let them come into my heart, to be cleansed and comforted there, to be renewed in hope and peace and love.

"I am their mother, as well as yours. I am the mother of all the afflicted and the sorrowing. I am the mother of those innocents, and of all the martyrs who will die for you.

"I am their mother. Be you their brother."

CHAPTER XI

When Herod died, an angel notified Joseph, in a dream, that it would be safe to take his family home. Archelaus had succeeded his father as king of Judea, and he was as murderous a maniac as Herod. The angel, therefore advised Joseph to return not to Bethlehem but to Nazareth.

It cannot be said that the Nazarenes greeted the return of Mary and Joseph with any great show of enthusiasm. Nazareth was not a town noted for hospitality.

"Have you been away?" some of the men asked Joseph. Others scolded him because they had work they wanted him to do, and he was gone. He had left the people without a carpenter. He must not do that again. Some of the women complained bitterly to Mary. "I wanted you to come and bake some bread for me, and you were not here. . . . I had such a sharp pain in my side! And I went to see you, but there was never anyone home; I had to suffer all by myself! . . . I sent the children to get you, but you'd gone. I wanted you to help me mend some of my clothes. You would take just that time to go on a holiday."

Few people said anything about the Baby. Babies were plentiful in Nazareth; though Jesus was the only one with such a beautiful cradle. The sight of that cradle created envy in the hearts of many parents; and envy engendered other bad feelings.

Besides, every mother and father realized at once that Jesus was a better Baby in every way than any one of theirs; but they would rather die than admit it.

Lucifer, however, knew the Child was perfect. Lucifer, once the brightest and most beautiful angel in heaven, could not be fooled. This Infant was so infuriatingly beautiful the devil wanted to destroy him every time he saw him. But he held himself in check. It would be foolish. He had beaten himself by acting too hastily before. He must have patience — though he hated the sound of the word. The Baby, if he lived, would give him some inkling of the Most High's strategy. So, in a manner of speaking, it was good he had escaped the massacre.

Two things irked Lucifer beyond all bearing. He could seldom come anywhere near the Child, because of Mary, and also because of Joseph. The woman shed an intolerable light. Her husband shed a strong light too, and it kept growing stronger. It was this light that made the lord of hell hate Joseph with a most unholy hate, and to suspect him of heroic sanctity. Once Lucifer had almost made up his mind that this strong and virile young man had taken a vow of virginity, even as his wife had done. But to Lucifer that was too utterly ridiculous! And then — the way he looked at the Child! Lucifer was convinced the little one was Joseph's own flesh and blood. No, Joseph could not possibly be a virgin. Then why did he remind the devil of St. Michael the archangel?

Lucifer could never get close enough to the Baby in his ornate cradle — with its star of David and its royal purple bunch of grapes. When he did, he knew a sickly feeling of embarrassment, an abasement that was murder to his pride, and a feeling of utter helplessness. But it showed him the Most High had great plans for this Child.

Once when Joseph was at work and Mary had taken the Baby with her to the well, Lucifer entered the house with the intention of kicking the cradle to pieces. He would have done it too, had it not been for those painted grapes. They were some sort of symbol, a key to something the Almighty planned to do, something still secret from all the powers of hell. The mighty angel of the damned shrank from that symbol!

All the devil could do was to post spies around the house, and all over Nazareth and the hamlets and towns nearby. They were to report constantly, and in full.

Their reports were contradictory. The Child, some of the imps asserted, was the most popular in all Galilee. All the other children, boys and girls, followed him, obeyed him, imitated him, loved him. It was sickening, these said, to see what influence the Boy had on his companions. He was making them so good that an imp couldn't do anything with them.

Other imps, just as unreliable as the first batch, said Jesus was becoming more and more unpopular as he grew up. Mothers could not abide him, for he outshone their darlings in every way. Fathers distrusted him because he thrilled and awed their daughters without paying any attention to them. And many people avoided him because they felt uncomfortable in his presence.

A third set of imps reported that the Boy was unusually strong, abnormally intelligent, and scandalously in love with God and all God had created. He loved trees and shrubs and wild flowers. He loved stones and hills and dust and rain. He loved the sun and the moon and the stars. He loved the Jordan river and the lake of Tiberias. He loved birds and animals and men of all sorts — even sinners. Nay, he seemed to have a special love for sinners. The Boy was dangerous, they warned Lucifer. He was extremely dangerous. He should be immediately disposed of or he would do great harm to hell.

The devil decided, with a wisdom born not in hell but in the highest heaven, that he must wait the proper time to put this holy One to death. Killing him now would keep Lucifer from learning what God intended. Lucifer had to know God's plans, so he could thwart them.

Jesus was tall when he reached the age of twelve. Then, according to the Mosaic law, he acquired full religious obligations, and had to be considered no longer a mere boy but a grown-up man. He would go now, every year, to attend the Passover ceremonies in Jerusalem. He would travel with the men in the caravans, no longer with his mother.

This year Lucifer decided to accompany the caravan to and from Jerusalem, rather than entrust the business to his agents. The pilgrims were impossible. Every last one of them had been contaminated in some way by the holiness of Mary and Joseph, and that abominably holy Son of theirs. Yes, that One would certainly have to die a horrible death. But not yet. Not yet.

Lucifer didn't altogether regret all he suffered on the trip to Jerusalem; because Jesus stayed behind when his people started north, after the Passover. And because of this, the devil got a better idea of the danger that threatened hell. Also, he enjoyed the grief and fear and agony Mary and Joseph suffered when they learned they had lost Jesus.

Mary had been uneasy all that day. She had never before been away from Jesus for so long a time. This day he had been away from her for many hours. Every time the caravan turned the shoulder of a hill and gave her a chance to look forward to the men's section, she hoped for a sight of him and Joseph. But there was always some shambling camel in the way, some nervous donkey, some curious knot of men, or some blinding fog of dust. She looked at the sun from time to time, wondering what held it so steadily in the blue, what kept it from moving as it should. She longed, with a physical longing, to see it touch the horizon and explode into its millions of colors. For at sundown Joseph would come striding to her with that benediction in his eyes, and Jesus would be walking sedately at his side!

Or would he, now, be running like the little boy he was only a few short days ago? How they grew, these children of men! Before a mother realized it, her baby was a man with a mustache and a beard. How long would it be before her Son grew a beard like Joseph's?

Once upon a time Joshua had cried out, "Stand still, O sun, at Gabaon, O moon in the valley of Aialon." He had wanted time to destroy the armies of the Amorrite kings who menaced Israel. And God had listened, and had stayed the sun and the moon until Joshua had slaughtered the Amorrite hosts. Mary was almost tempted to cry, "Descend, O sun, this moment; O moon put a swift end to this weary day." She was almost tempted to add: "God, let the Sun of my life stand still too; don't let him grow away from me." But she was not really tempted. "Be it done according to thy will," she said. There was a joy in waiting, she mused, though there might be no contentment in that joy. There was the joy of anticipation. This would beget the joy of attainment. To live was to wait. To wait was to live.

Joseph, not finding Jesus among the men, thought he must be traveling with Mary. He was unselfishly glad of this, knowing how Mary missed the Boy. Joseph missed Jesus too. He felt abandoned, insufferably lonesome, and empty of heart. He too looked up and down the coils of the caravan whenever he could. But all he saw was a movement in the dust. Without Jesus, he thought, the world is dull of dust, everything is discolored or obscured, nothing looks real, and life is a bore. Without Jesus a man could not help feeling the dust of exile on his lips and on his tongue, and the weariness of life in the marrow of his bones. Without Jesus the caravan of the years would go joylessly onward to a joyless end. But this caravan, Joseph consoled himself, would halt at sundown. And he would see both Jesus and Mary! This was worth waiting for, even in emptiness and boredom.

The sun went down at last, like a pilot leaving the ship he had guided through the depths and the shoals of the day. The caravan crept around the base of a limestone cliff that overlooked a desolate rock valley. And immediately it broke up into many different parts, each part going its own separate way. Mary said a prayer of thanks, slipped out of the saddle, patted the donkey's neck affectionately, and stroked his long furry ears; at the same time looking for Joseph and her Son.

She saw Joseph, at last, with an odd sort of pain in her heart. He was alone! And there was a look in his eyes Mary could read without the least effort. "Where is Jesus?" that look asked her.

Thus the third sword came, like the others, suddenly, and in a moment of exquisite happiness. It was more cruel than the others, for it brought terror as well as anguish. And it opened anew the wounds made by the swords of Simeon and Herod, which she thought had healed. It was a merciless blade, and one almost impossible to bear, since Jesus was not there to give her strength and courage. Thank God for Joseph! Without him, she felt, she might have died.

Jesus had not stayed behind deliberately, Mary thought. He knew what his absence would mean to her and Joseph. He had never done anything to hurt them. He never would. He had been kidnapped. He had had an accident. He had been taken ill. The soldiers of King Herod had recognized him. And, knowing how Herod had once sought to destroy him, they had slain him as they slew the other babies ten years and more ago.

The Boy was nowhere in the camp. No one had seen him. No one knew where he might be. He had spoken to none of them about any plans he might have had. Mary and Joseph decided, without a word to each other, to return immediately to Jerusalem. It was dark and cold. There were dangerous places in the road. Evil men sometimes lay in wait for travelers in the night. They were thirty miles or more from Jerusalem, and they would have to walk, for the ass was tired and hungry. He was a slow-paced animal at best, however — and they must hurry. Joseph had walked all the way from Jerusalem, and he was as tired as the beast. He had not eaten, and now he could not eat. He was dying for sleep, but he could not think of food or sleep or danger or weariness or anything else.

They hurried along the narrow road, stumbling at times, at times coming close to the edge of an unseen hole in the road, or to the rim overlooking a deep abyss. Dark shapes moving across the hills beneath a powdered sky, speaking not to each other but only to the Lord on high. They entered Jerusalem as the morning star began to fade. The Temple greeted them in the dawn, shining white. The city decked itself in the beautiful streamers of the rising sun, and bade them hope. But its high dark walls frowned at them, and denied the promise of the sunrise.

They did not find him that day or the next. The city was, to them, a taunting, defying succession of stone stairways, stone walls, stone houses, stony hearts. Jerusalem is a rock, a cluster of rocks, a hill, a herd of hills. It is filled with caverns and devious holes. One goes down many steep flights of dark and narrow and twisting stairs to ask, "Have you seen Jesus?" One goes up those stairs, a little more tired than before, a little more sick at heart. One climbs high up to the quarters of other acquaintances and friends, only to hear the refrain that pounds upon the heart like a heavy hammer: "Jesus? No, he is not here."

He was not in any house or flat or hut or den they knew. He might be in the markets. They walked through these places many times, carefully searching the narrow, filthy, smelly, crowded streets that went up and down through the rows of shops and stores and counters. They walked in the middle of the street when they could, in the gutters when they must, treading on rotting bits of vegetables and meats the merchants had thrown away. Overloaded donkeys pressed them tightly against dusty walls or against cluttered counters displaying wares of all kinds. A shepherd with a flock of sheep shoved them aside roughly, that his animals might pass — Joseph doing nothing to show his resentment except to keep Mary from being touched by the shepherd or the sheep. A Roman chariot almost ran them down. Packs of dogs barked at them and threatened them; and sometimes packs of boys came rushing toward them — ragged, noisy, dirty, furtive, thieving gamins.

They questioned many people, Jews, Romans, Egyptians, Parthians, Greeks, freemen, slaves, beggars, soldiers, Temple guards, the hagglers in the markets. No one had seen him. No boy had been imprisoned recently. No boy had been killed or hurt. No boy had been put to death by the soldiers.

"We may have passed him on the road," Joseph thought. "He might have been hurrying to overtake the caravan, and, in the darkness, failed to see us; as we failed to see him."

"If so," Mary said, "he will come back, even as we did; and he will find us."

They found him, at last, in the Temple. He was talking with a group of distinguished men, priests, scholars, professors, doctors of the Law. He was talking with authority. And the great men about him listened with marked respect and wonder!

Mary and Joseph heard his voice before they saw him. They came to life, like dying plants in a tired and rocky soil when a gentle rain falls on them. Their bodies straightened. Their limbs took on fresh strength. Their eyes shone. Their faces shed a dozen years or more. They hurried forward, but checked themselves, suddenly conscious that their Jesus was a little boy no longer.

Lucifer, who had been highly entertained by the confusion and dismay and shame and anger of the learned ones in the presence of this tremendous Intellect, left the gathering quickly.

Mary could not move forward because she suddenly realized that Jesus had left her and Joseph — and all their friends and relatives in the caravan — because he had wanted to! He had not been kidnapped. He had not been lured away. He had departed of his own free will — to talk to these lights of Israel! Had he spent all his time with them?

Joseph could not move either, at first; for the mere sight of the Boy had put a happy spell on him. He was like one petrified. Finally Jesus saw him and Mary, and the spell was broken.

Jesus came toward them, through the crowd of priests and doctors; and Mary all but rushed to him. Yet she restrained herself. An ordinary mother would have taken him in her arms and hugged and kissed him fervently. Then she would have spanked him thoroughly. Mary greeted him with only a motherly reproach: "Son, why have you done this to us? Your father and I have sought you, sorrowing."

And now the sword was twisted cruelly in her heart; for Jesus did not look at her as he had always looked before.

"How is it that you sought me?" he asked her. "Did you not know I must be about my Father's business?"

Before she could reply Jesus turned to those he had been teaching, and waved his hand to them, not so much as a gesture of farewell as of dismissal. Then, linking arms with Mary and Joseph, he went happily out of the Temple with them.

Lucifer watched from a distance, and returned to the teachers. He put one thought in each of them: "That is no ordinary boy. His is no ordinary human mind. He speaks by Beelzebub, the prince of devils. I sensed that immediately, that's why I didn't argue with him too much, as those pompous old pots did. Those poor mildewed minds trying to wrestle with the devil! It was almost funny. But they deserved the asses' ears the boy gave them. No one should try to argue with the devil. This boy should be watched. And his parents. They too must be possessed."

CHAPTER XII

Jesus went willingly back to Nazareth with Mary and Joseph and was subject to them until that appointed day when he went forth into the world to conclude his Father's business. And in this period of his life, some theologians say, he gave more glory to his Father than he did in his passion, death, and resurrection.

God loves humility and obedience; and Jesus was the humblest and most obedient of all his children. He was a dutiful Son to Mary and Joseph — and at the same time he was constantly attending to the business of his Father in heaven.

It took Mary a long time to understand what Jesus meant when he spoke of this business. And understanding brought another twist of the swords in her heart.

The Father's business was the education, conversion, and redemption of the world. Jesus, the Word of God, must teach all men that God loved them and wanted them to love him; and that only by loving and being loved could they be happy here and hereafter.

And Jesus, as the Agent, the Son, and the full Partner of God the Father, must offer Himself as a willing holocaust to redeem all men, and make them eligible for heaven! Jesus must die that sinners might gain eternal life! That was the Father's business!

God the Father had been offended by the sins of men. His

justice demanded infinite reparation, infinite expiation. It was impossible for any man to make such atonement — for every man, however holy he might be, was tainted with original sin. And no man could give infinite satisfaction to God's justice, since no man had infinite love or infinite remorse.

Only Jesus, of all men born of woman, could offer full and complete compensation for the sins of men. And God, whose mercy and love for men is as limitless as his justice, would accept the offer of his Son, Jesus. It was for this that the Son of God had been born a man — that he could die for men!

She had not always understood him. But what mother does fully understand her son? All children are mysteries to their parents; and Jesus was the most mysterious of all, for he was God as well as a child. He lived in heaven and on earth. He lived in eternity and time. Of course she had forgotten Simeon's words in the wonder and delight of bringing up her Son.

"I should have known," she thought, "I did know once. Twice. I knew that he must die. And on the cross! But I let my knowledge rust. I must not forget again. I must keep my knowledge as bright as the swords that brought it to me.

"That is why he deserted me and Joseph in Jerusalem. He wanted to prepare us for that awful day when the business has been established. And oh, he wanted us to experience the joy of finding him at last!

"He thinks always of his Father, and of his Father's love for sinners. He thinks always of the price he must pay to start his Father's business. Every thought must be a cruel thorn pressed deep into his mind. A crown of thorns! I shall wear one too. Who has a better right than I, his mother? And what nobler crown could any woman wear — if she wear it for her children?"

Jesus grew like any other boy, in wisdom and grace and experience and stature. God never acts too slowly, nor too early. He is in no hurry. He has no hothouses nor forcing beds. He permits nature to act for him. Nor does he act too late. He has his own timetables and they serve him admirably.

Jesus had to be mature to command the attention and respect of the world he had come to redeem. He had to be sturdy enough to walk barefooted all over his kingdom, to do without sleep for many nights and days, to fast for lengthy periods, and to endure the tortures waiting for him. He had to know, intimately, all that was noble in men, all that was weak and shameful, all that was hard to bear. He had to know, as a man, the ambitions, the desires, the motives of all men.

The characters that would be associated with him in the drama of redemption had to have achieved that ripeness of good and evil, and strength and weakness, that would permit them to play the roles assigned them.

And Joseph, who had so well enacted the part of the foster father and protector had to be rewarded by God the Father, with a seat where he could watch the other players; and where he could, in full comfort, understand and appreciate and applaud every line and every bit of business the divine hand had written in the script.

Joseph was a poor man. He worked hard, like all the other Jews in Rome-run Palestine. He was forced to submit to insults, privations, vexations, extortions, and great and petty tyrannies. Sometimes he and his family hadn't enough to eat — for Joseph was generous to the poor. Sometimes he suffered from the cold, for he had given away a warm cloak or had outworn it. Yet he was the most fortunate of men; and he knew it. He was happier, even in the most dire periods of his poverty, than any of the wealthy rulers of the world.

When he came home from work, the most beautiful woman ever born was waiting to welcome him. She, who would become the queen of heaven, looked upon him as her lord and king. She washed and dried his feet. She placed a well-cooked dinner on the table for him, a clean table in a spotlessly clean room. And she never failed to let him see she loved him.

Jesus would welcome him too. When very young, he used to rush out of the house, throw himself into Joseph's arms, and hug him; he loved to pull Joseph's beard and rumple his hair. And he loved to pour the purifying water over Joseph's wrists, in the orthodox ritual way, before they sat down to dinner.

After dinner there would be long conversations about the prophets and the poets of Holy Writ, and about God the Father and his thirst for the love of men; and often Mary and the Boy would ask Joseph to sing one of the many hymns he knew.

Sometimes, it seemed to Joseph, the stars lowered themselves to hear every word sung or chanted or whispered in that humble little grotto in the rock; and to learn, from the faces of Mary and Jesus, the way stars ought to shine.

As he lived, so he died — with Mary and Jesus close to him, shining their faces on him. This time it was a band of angels that lowered themselves into the room, cherubim and seraphim brighter than the stars. They were singing, but the music was faint; and he had to strain to catch their words. He repeated them slowly:

"Behold, my beloved speaketh to me; Arise, make haste, my love, my dove, and come. For winter is now past, the rain is over and gone. The flowers have appeared in our land, the time of pruning is come. . . ."

He looked at Mary, a long last look. He filled his soul with her. He looked at Jesus. "You came from one heaven to another," he said. "I saw that when you were born. I knew it by the way you looked at her. I too. I go from one heaven to another."

He smiled as though he were supremely happy. For a moment he was David: "He shall come down like rain upon the fleece; and as showers falling gently upon the earth. In his days shall justice spring up, and abundance of peace, till the moon be taken away. And he shall rule from sea to sea, and from the river unto the ends of the earth."

And he was Isaias: "The wolf shall dwell with the lamb, and the leopard shall lie down with the kid; the calf and the lion and the sheep shall abide together, and a little child shall lead them."

And he was Job: "For I know that my Redeemer liveth, and in the last day I shall rise out of the earth. And I shall be clothed again with my skin, and in my flesh I shall see God. Whom I myself shall see, and my eyes shall behold, and not another; this my hope is laid up in my bosom."

And he was Solomon: "If a man should give all the substance of his house for love, he shall despise it as nothing. . . . 'Til the day break and the shadows retire, I will go to the mountain of myrrh. . . ."

Mary wept in the arms of her Son. Yet she rejoiced. Joseph was dead, but he had never been so close to her. She was a widow, yet the memory of his love would warm her all the rest of her life; and it would give her strength and courage in the dreadful days to come, as it had when Jesus was a boy of twelve.

After the body had been properly entombed, the family gathered to decide what should be done about Joseph's Son. Jesus was thirty then, stalwart and strong and able, a skillful carpenter, and a devoted and obedient Son. But he wanted to leave his mother and go off somewhere into the desert and set the world afire! Some of his older relatives, near kin of Mary and of Joseph, were concerned about him. He was a visionary, they said, an impractical dreamer like his father, Joseph. Joseph had dreamed about angels telling him to go here, go there, do this, and do that. And he had gone to considerable trouble and expense because he believed those dreams.

Jesus frightened them. He kept saying the strangest things.

He had come to set the world afire, he said. He had come to
bring not peace but a sword. Words like that. Did he think he
could burn down Rome and all its mighty empire, and make
Israel the ruler of the world? Did he think he could put all
Israel's enemies to the sword? One humble Jewish carpenter
was challenging the entire world! Was that sane? His mother
needed him. He should remain at the work his father taught
him. How proud Joseph had been, watching him in the carpenter
shop! What would Joseph say now, if he knew the notions in his
poor Son's mind?

The younger kin disagreed. They thought Jesus should have
the chance to do as he wished. Among these were his cousins,
who were known as his sisters and brothers. Four of them,
Simon, Jude, James, and Joseph, later gave him more than a
chance. They gave him their lives.

They would see that Mary was not too lonesome, these young
people said, and that she lacked for nothing. Let Jesus go. They
knew nothing about his ideas or his plans. But they knew him.
They loved him. And they had a profound respect for him, even
when they thought he was wrong. Let him go. He would come
back when this dream was over. And he would be all the better
for the adventure.

He was a dreamer, of course. But he wasn't the only dreamer
in the land. Men were talking about a prophet called John the
Baptist, who, like Jesus, believed the Kingdom of God was at
hand; and who called on the people to repent, to confess their
sins, and to be baptized in the river Jordan. He too dreamed of
remaking the world.

Jesus listened silently as his kin quarreled over Him, trying
to shape his future according to their own inclinations and ideas
of what was right and proper or hoping to give him the opportunity of escaping, if only for a little time, from the routine
of a worker in a very little town in Galilee. And he knew, both

as man and God, what millions of his followers would have to
suffer before their families stopped trying to prevent their giving
themselves to God as priests, nuns, Brothers, or members of a
lay apostolate.

Eventually one of the uncles, a crafty man who thought he
knew how to solve the problem, suggested that Mary be the one
to say yea or nay to her son's silly dream of conquering the
unconquerable world. Two things he did not know — two things
nobody knew but Mary and Joseph. They did not know Jesus
was the Lord. They did not know Mary was not only His mother,
but His most obedient handmaid as well.

She faced them calmly.

"The word of God has come to John in the wilderness," she
said. "That is why he preaches repentance and baptism. John
is he of whom it is written, 'Behold I send my angel before thy
face, who shall prepare the world before thee.' John is the son of
Zachary, the priest, and of Elizabeth, my cousin. The angel of
the Lord, my cousin's son, waits in the wilderness for his Lord.
My Son will visit him. The Kingdom of God is at hand indeed!"

She turned a serene and smiling face to Jesus.

"Go now, my Son," she said, "for a light of revelation to the
gentiles and the glory of thy people, Israel."

Nobody but Jesus knew what she meant. He kissed her fondly,
held her hands a moment, bowed courteously to all his kindred,
bent his head in a solemn prayer, and strode majestically through
the door.

CHAPTER XIII

"And in those days," wrote St. Matthew, "cometh John the Baptist preaching in the desert of Judea, and saying: Do penance: for the kingdom of heaven is at hand. . . . Then went out to him Jerusalem and all Judea, and all the country about Jordan; and were baptized by him in the Jordan, confessing their sins."

And Lucifer also went out to him, traveling with friendly Sadducees and Pharisees, not merely to satisfy his curiosity but also to do something about this preacher and his preaching, and those traitorous ones who were confessing their sins. His imps had been making exaggerated reports about this man, and about his growing menace to Lucifer's long reign; but he had paid scant attention. He had been busy at a work he loved, increasing the bitter hatred that already existed between Jerusalem and Rome, between Church and State, between the high priests and the Sanhedrin on the one side and Pontius Pilate on the other.

He foresaw that he would soon have a battle to the death with the Man called Jesus. And whether this Man was or was not the Son of God, Lucifer would need all the help he could muster. He would need the Sanhedrin and the high priests, especially Annas and his son-in-law, Caiphas. And he would need Pontius Pilate. His strategy was to force Jesus into a position where he would be ground to extinction between these two forces. He had prepared everything well. He was so proud of himself he found it difficult to associate with these poor miserable priests and scholars, even though, in their own stupid human way, they had as much pride as any of his imps.

He felt he had but to spread his great black wings over the Jordan, and the preacher, and all the sniveling sinners who had come to hear him; and that immediately the nonsense would stop. The preacher would falter in his talk. And the sheep would run baaing away in all directions, each doing his best to get back to Lucifer's comfortable fold as soon as possible, and to stay there — forever. Aye, for ever and ever and ever!

But he had made a mistake. He realized this when he heard the preacher's voice. He and his friends were a long way off at that time, but the words were clear.

"Repent!" John was shouting. "Repent, for the Kingdom of God is at hand!"

Lucifer shook, knowing the power in that voice was the power of the Holy Ghost. His pride collapsed. His angelic wits were thrown into disorder and confusion. The kingdom of heaven was at hand!

It was his own fault. While he was getting ready to fight the Most High in Nazareth and Jerusalem, the Most High had attacked him here in the desert. His whole flank was threatened. His entire army might be routed.

Never since Isaias wrote those insulting and degrading lines about him had Lucifer known such abasing humiliation, such helpless fury. He felt the old prophet was mocking him anew — even as he listened to this new prophet, John.

"How art thou fallen from heaven, O Lucifer," Isaias had taunted him, "who didst rise in the morning! How are thou fallen to the earth, that didst wound the nations. And thou saidst in thy heart, I will ascend into heaven, I will exalt my throne above the stars of God, I will sit in the mountain of the covenant.

. . . I will ascend above the height of the clouds, I will be like the Most High. But yet thou shalt be brought down to hell, into the depths of the pit."

Lucifer gibbered like a scalded monkey. He hissed like a den of vipers. He whimpered like a spanked and half-starved puppy.

There was a great crowd about the Baptist, and men were showing tears of contrition as they descended into the water. Some were asking John, "What shall I do to be saved?" And he was telling them! These souls might be lost to hell forever. Through their confession of sins! Through their tears! And through that cleansing water!

Lucifer sensed disaster in that water. It might indeed ruin him if God used water to wash away the sins of men. Was that what God had in mind? Lucifer did not know. Therein lay his own particular hell.

John was a tall man with the noblest head in all the world — the noblest save one. Lucifer knew him now. He was that son of the priest, Zachary, born when both his parents were old enough to be his great-grandparents. And — alas! How could such a brilliant intellect as Lucifer's forget it — he had been filled with the Holy Ghost while yet in his mother's womb!

He was a kin of Jesus. Was he the Son of God, this John the Baptist?

John had spent many years in this wilderness about the Jordan and the Dead Sea. He had lived in the holes in the barren rocks and crags and cliffs. He had lived on dried locusts and wild honey. He had fashioned a leather girdle about his loins and woven himself a cloak of camel's hair. He had lived in penance and piety. He must have spoken often to the Most High. Had he learned about Baptism from God? Was it God who sent him here to convert sinners?

Lucifer felt like crying out to the Lord that he had been caught napping. But his pride forbade this. His anger began to grow.

Guile came back to him, giving him increasing confidence. He had suffered a most humbling defeat, but so long as he had to deal with mere men — even though they were men sent by God — he might still win the final battle.

He began to study John. He was like the desert itself. Hard. Austere. Unyielding. Uncompromising. Defiant. Filled with mystery and awe — and the power of God. A hairy man. A man like Elias of old. A shaggy man. One who cared nothing for the earth. One concerned entirely with heaven.

"I will strike off his head," Lucifer promised himself. "And I will play with it. I will dance with it before all the world!" His friends, the Pharisees and Sadducees, had threaded their way slowly through the crowd of common people, being careful not to touch any of them or brush against them — thus defiling themselves — and were about to question the preacher when he roared at them: "You brood of vipers!"

They stopped in mid-step as though lightning had flashed from John's great mouth, with the thunder of his voice, and had blasted them.

"Who has shown you how to flee from the wrath to come?" John demanded.

He glared at them, demanding they repent their sins, and bring forth good fruits. They thought themselves among the elect of God because they had Abraham for a father — and needed not to perform good works. But God, he shouted, could raise up children to Abraham out of the stones all about them.

Lucifer looked at those stones and then at his friends. The comparison, he had to admit, was apt. The stones were as hard and as dull and cold and unfeeling as these masters of Israel.

He conceived, in spite of himself, a great admiration for John — and, at the same time, a good way to get rid of him. He would bring Herod, the tetrarch of Galilee, to the Jordan. Herod was a messy sort of sinner. He wasn't bloodthirsty like his father —

more's the pity! But he was sinner enough for Lucifer's purposes, since he was a sot and a scoundrel and a seducer. He had stolen Herodias, his brother's wife. John had only to look at him with his fierce soul-seeing eyes to denounce him as bitterly as he had denounced the Pharisees and Sadducees. Then Herod would put John in prison for his wife's sake. He would not kill the prophet, since he was a superstitious sort. He would be afraid that John would haunt him. But he would be even more frightened of Herodias. He would do what she wanted. Herodias was hell's own darling. She would demand John's head as a trophy, Lucifer was sure.

He listened eagerly to the Baptist.

"For now the ax is laid at the root of the trees," John said. "Every tree, therefore, that doth not yield good fruit shall be cut down and cast into the fire."

There might be a new religion, Lucifer thought, but hell would still be fed the dead wood of rotten souls.

"I baptize in water unto penance," John said, "but He that shall come after me is mightier than I, whose shoes I am not worthy to bear." The thunder in John's voice softened to the whisper of a lover. The harshness left his face. "He shall baptize you in fire and the Holy Ghost. His fan is in his hand. He will thoroughly cleanse his threshing floor. He will store the wheat into the barn. But the chaff fanned from the grain he will burn with unquenchable fire."

A new religion indeed. Baptism by water and fire and the Holy Ghost! Lucifer began to tremble again. But there was some comfort in John's words. The unquenchable fire could mean only the fire of hell. All the world might be baptized in the new religion, but good old human nature would keep Lucifer on his throne.

Who was the One to come after John? Jesus, undoubtedly — unless John had lied purposely to deceive the devil. A saint would do that. Lucifer, prince of lies, had detected in John's words nothing but the truth. Still — John might feel all's fair in war. And this was war.

Did it matter which was the mightier of the two? Both had been easy to approach. Both were mortal men. Both had to die sometime. The sooner the better! One he would kill by a sword shaped like a cross, the other on a cross shaped like a sword. The new religion would, naturally, die with them!

He made an effort to stop trembling; but it was beyond him. The very name of the Holy Ghost made him shiver and shake. And if it were true that the world would be baptized in him — but by what authority did this last of the prophets speak?

"Art thou the Christ?" one of the priests asked.

"I am not."

Was he lying? Lucifer didn't know. That exasperated him.

"What then? Art thou Elias?"

"No."

"Art thou the prophet spoken of by Moses?"

"Indeed not."

"Then who art thou? We must report to those who sent us here. What sayest thou of thyself?"

"I am the voice of one crying in the wilderness; Make straight the way of the Lord, as said the prophet Isaias!"

Lucifer was enraged anew at the mention of that name.

"For that, holy preacher," he promised, "I will have Herodias give your head to her dogs!"

"Make ready the way of the Lord," John thundered. "Make straight his paths. Every valley shall be filled, and every mountain and hill shall be brought low. And the crooked ways shall be made straight, and the rough ways smooth; and all mankind shall see the Salvation of God."

At that moment Lucifer observed Jesus coming toward the river. Was this the Salvation of God? Was this the Lord for whom the paths should be made straight? He looked like a simple, ordinary, healthy workingman. He wore a white seamless robe, and a white linen covering over his long hair. But there was something so wonderful about him that even those engrossed in the words of John turned to look at him. He carried himself like a king. Like a god, Lucifer thought. If he could make a god like this, out of wood or stone or iron, or even clay, he would have no trouble making the nations bow down and adore it.

Perhaps he actually was the Son of God — God himself made man!

Lucifer, who could turn himself into a serpent or a dog or a flea, wished he could change into a grain of sand so he could hide beneath a stone. But he knew, even as he scoffed at the thought, that, whatever he did, God would see him. All he could do was to shrivel and shrink and shudder.

John stopped shouting. He stared at Jesus, then hastened to meet him. They walked to the Jordan together, conversing amiably, not as old friends, however, but more like two strangers who had recognized something familiar in one another. And each, it seemed, wanted to be baptized by the other!

Lucifer wanted to fly away; but his fiendish curiosity would not permit him to leave. Here were two powerful enemy generals conferring together on a campaign against him. He must stay to learn their plans, if he could. Each wanted to begin the campaign with baptism! Truly this must be a powerful new weapon. He must find out all he could about it.

It was Jesus who went into the water to be baptized "in remission of sin." Could this really be the Son of God? No! That would be too fantastic — too divinely fantastic!

Jesus came up from the water. His face was so bright it blinded and tortured Lucifer — who once had been the light-bearer before God's throne. The heavens were opened. The Holy Ghost descended on Jesus, in the form of a dove, and rested on him.

And a voice from heaven said, so plainly Lucifer could hear it, "This is my beloved Son in whom I am well pleased."

Lucifer could not see on which head the Holy Ghost had alighted. In that light was the Triune God, Father, Son, and Holy Ghost! Lucifer was powerless to do anything but prostrate himself in adoration, like all the other angels. He threw himself, proud spirit though he was, onto the dust and mud and sand and stones of the Jordan bank.

When he lifted himself, at last, Jesus had gone; and John was baptizing. Lucifer decided he must follow Jesus. John would not go away. He could always be found here. He would stay in this spotlight of the world, shouting, "Repent, repent." He did not go to the world. The world came to him. He drew them with the power of the Holy Ghost! Perhaps Jesus also was filled with the Holy Ghost?

Lucifer swelled with pride and grew with fury. And now that the Triune God was no longer crushing him into the earth, he screamed defiance.

CHAPTER XIV

Jesus, filled with the Holy Spirit, and with the joy of his Father's voice — "Thou art my beloved Son in whom I am well pleased" — went into the desert where John had spent so many years. He began his ministry by forty days and nights spent in fasting and prayer. And Lucifer, with the permission of the Most High, followed him into the wilderness to tempt him.

Lucifer was appalled by the holiness of this Man, and by his prayers for sinners. He attacked repeatedly, only to be ignored or snubbed or scorned. But on the last day he felt he had a customer, and might make a sale. This Man, human or divine, must be ravenously hungry!

"If thou art the Son of God," he said, "command that these stones become loaves of bread."

The power of the devil is great. He could have brought fresh bread into the desert, and savory meats, and luscious fruits and vegetables such as Jesus' mother had served him, and the choicest wines — thus tempting the hungry man to the sin of gluttony.

But he wanted Jesus to prove himself. He wanted him to show his power over all nature. He wanted him to perform a miracle for the sake of his empty human stomach — and for the sake of his human pride. Surely the Man must have some pride in him?

Surely, if he were the Son of God, he would delight in confounding his enemy.

But Jesus answered, not like one far superior to the devil, but like the humblest of men; "It is written, 'Not in bread alone doth man live, but by every word that proceedeth from the mouth of God.'"

The devil never gives up. He took Jesus into Jerusalem and set him on a pinnacle of the temple. Jesus had made no effort to resist being carried away by the wicked angel, knowing his Father had permitted it.

"Now," Lucifer said, "if thou be the Son of God, cast thyself down, for it is written: 'He hath given his angels charge over thee, and in their hands they shall bear thee up, lest perhaps thou dash thy foot against a stone.'"

Jesus could have told the devil that, though he would not change stones into bread, he would, very soon, change bread into his own Body, and would feed his children with It. He could have said that, though he would not cast himself down from this dizzying height, he would, in due time, descend from the highest heaven, whenever he was called upon to do so, into the hands of any one of his priests, that he might be given to all his people. His, not Lucifer's.

He had no intention of throwing himself down into the multitudes of people in the court below. His Father had not intended him to come in miraculous and spectacular glory to the world, a man borne up by angels. It was quite the opposite. He had selected a stable for him, a hole in a rock. He had summoned only a few poor shepherds to rejoice at his birth. He had reared him in poverty. And he had hidden him, most of his life, in a little town in Galilee, the least known and least loved part of Israel.

"It is written again," Jesus said quietly, "'Thou shalt not tempt the Lord thy God!'"

Lucifer was not discouraged. Every man, he believed could be tempted by offers of majesty, power, immense wealth, unlimited glory. Therefore he took Jesus up into a very high mountain and showed him all the kingdoms of the world — "And the glory of them."

"All these," he said, expansively, as one who owned the world and could give it to anyone he favored, "will I give thee, if, falling down, thou wilt adore me!"

Poor Lucifer! He still hoped to put himself on a level with almighty God — or to reach a higher level! Now, if he could induce the Son of the Almighty to bend a knee to him. . . .

Lucifer knew men better than they knew themselves. Many had adored him willingly, devotedly, shamelessly, for a fraction of what he promised now. Surely the human part of this Man would respond in some way to the lure of pomp and power?

He waited in an agony of torture for the answer of the Lord. He might win the most tremendous victory of his existence in the next second. Or he might be doomed to a hell a hundredfold as hellish as he knew, because of his impudence and blasphemy.

Jesus could have made it clear that Lucifer had no power over men, save that given him by the free will God had placed in every soul; that he had dominion only over hell. He might have forewarned him that the waters of baptism could quench the flames of hell that menaced sinners, for those waters carried grace. He might have let Lucifer see that in the future men would reckon time with regard to the Son of God, not to the Lord of hell.

But all he said was, "Begone, Satan; for it is written: 'The Lord thy God shalt thou adore, and him only shalt thou serve.'"

The devil had, and still has, a dozen or more names known to men. Jesus used none of them. Satan, the name he chose, is a Hebrew word meaning "enemy."

The devil left him then, as ordered. Hell quaked with his

frustration and his anger and his hatred. And new volcanoes vomitted molten lava into all his realms, that the damned might share his humiliation and fury, and his desire for revenge.

Then angels came and ministered to Jesus, giving him food and drink, and bringing him back to the Jordan, where John the Baptist was still crying to the world to repent and do penance for its sins.

Priests and levites were still asking John who he was, and why he baptized. And Jesus heard him reply: "I baptize with water; but in the midst of you there hath stood One whom you do not know. The same is he that shall come after me, who is preferred before me; the latchet of whose shoe I am not worthy to loose."

The next day John saw Jesus coming toward him, and he cried out to the group around him and the multitudes waiting their turns to be baptized: "Behold the Lamb of God," he cried — and people coming from all over Judea, and still far away from him, heard his words. "Behold him who taketh away the sin of the world. This is he of whom I said 'After me there cometh a man, who is preferred before me; because he was before me'; and I knew him not, but that he may be made manifest in Israel, therefore am I come baptizing with water.

"I saw the Holy Spirit coming down, as a dove, from heaven, and he remained upon him. . . . He who sent me to baptize with water said to me; 'He upon whom thou shalt see the Spirit descending, and remaining upon him, he it is that baptizeth with the Holy Ghost. And I saw, and I gave testimony that this is the Son of God!"

Lucifer heard. And still he was uncertain. It is his punishment that he can trust nobody, not even himself. Jesus might be the Son of God, but he had shown no proof of it. If he had been born of a virgin, Lucifer could not have doubted his divinity. But his mother had married!

In the days that followed, Lucifer noticed that Jesus had acquired a few disciples. He marveled at how easily the Man attracted other men; and how many he attracted. And he noted fearfully that Jesus treated men as though he were indeed the Son of God. If he could make all men think he was divine he would leave not a single soul on earth to worship the devil.

Lucifer must spread the word that Jesus was an ordinary man, there was no godhead in him. Let the world think of him as a good man, a good teacher, a gifted preacher, even a prophet able to perform miracles. Let them regard him as a sincere fanatic, or a great reformer with an original but impractical philosophy. Cancel the Man's divinity, and the world would remain the pleasure ground of hell.

He watched two disciples of John the Baptist as they followed Jesus near the river Jordan. They had heard the Baptist call him "the Lamb of God"; and they could not help following. It was the springtime of Christianity, and the young men were in the springtime of their first great love — the love of Jesus. They did not know he was Love Incarnate. They knew only that they wanted to belong to him, now and forever.

They were so obviously in love that Lucifer wanted to attack them. God might use love as a force to regain his kingdom; but Lucifer never would. There was no love in hell; there never would be; and if he had his way, there would be no love on earth.

The young men, John and Andrew, spent the day with Jesus; and they brought friends to meet him. One was Andrew's brother Simon. Jesus immediately changed this disciple's name. There was something too soft, too timid, in the name Simon. Jesus gave him a name with no softness in it, and no timidity. "Thou shalt be called Peter," he said. Peter means a rock. He did not ask Simon if he wanted to be turned into a rock. He acted as his Father did when he changed Abram into Abraham, and Jacob into Israel.

He met Philip the following day, and said only two words to him: "Follow me." Philip followed without a question. Philip spoke to Nathaniel about his friend Jesus of Nazareth, calling him "the Messiah." Nathaniel gagged on the name of Nazareth. Evidently the town had few admirers in Galilee. "Can anything good come out of Nazareth?" he asked. "Come and see," Philip answered. And Nathaniel came.

Jesus was glad to see him. "Behold an Israelite in whom there is no guile," he said to him. Nathaniel was startled. "I saw you before Philip called you," Jesus said, "when you were under the fig tree."

"Rabbi, thou art the Son of God," Nathaniel answered, impulsively, "thou art the king of Israel."

Jesus smiled at him. "You believe me," he said, "because I said I saw you under the fig tree. You will see greater things. Amen, amen, I say to you, you shall see the heavens opened, and the angels of God ascending the descending upon the Son of man."

Nathaniel did not know that Jesus was the only-begotten Son of God. He meant only that he was a holy man, a special or favorite son of the Most High, and one distinguished from other sons of God.

Paradoxically the words "Son of God" signified a man, any man, even a wretched sinner; whereas the words "Son of man" had only one meaning — that given it by the prophet Daniel:

"I beheld therefore in the vision of the night, and, lo, one like the son of man came with the clouds of heaven, and he came even to the Ancient of days; and they presented him before him. And he gave him power, and glory, and a kingdom; and all peoples, tribes and tongues shall serve him; his power is an everlasting power that shall not be taken away; and his kingdom that shall not be destroyed."

By calling himself the Son of man, Jesus proclaimed that his

Father, the Ancient of days, had given him the kingdom, and the power, and the glory, for ever and ever; he was the Lord, and the Judge of the world.

A few days later, at a marriage in Cana, Nathaniel saw the Lord's first public miracle.

CHAPTER XV

There was a mist in Nazareth that morning, so thick it shut out the hilltops circling the village. The first rays of the sun were making fantastic changes in it as Mary started home from the well. Her heart was full of wonder at God's power, and his artistry, and his love. See how he was coloring the fog for her! He seemed to be inviting her to walk through a rainbow into his arms.

When she saw the three men waiting in front of her home, she unconsciously increased her pace. They were vague figures; but something about them reminded her of the wise men who had come from the East so many many years ago, bringing rich presents for her Infant Jesus! Perhaps it was their attitude of expectancy, of reverence, and of utter amazement. The Magi had shown the same emotions as they stood outside the poor little house in Bethlehem — the most wretched dwelling under the most brilliant of stars. She would not have been surprised to see a train of dromedaries break through the fog.

As she came closer, and the visitors became less vague, she saw that one was young, a boy of 19 or 20. The others were somewhat older. Her heart beat fast at sight of the boy. He stood the way Jesus stood. He had almost the kingly grace of her Son, almost his poise. He had the same appearance of complete relaxation and an intense awareness and alertness. He seemed the most peaceful person on earth, and one prepared for anything that might happen.

As she neared them the young man went to her, and relieved her of the jar of water.

"I am John, the son of Zebedee, of Bethsaida," he said. "One of the disciples of the Rabbi Jesus. These are my friends, Simon and Andrew, sons of Jonas. They too are disciples of the Rabbi. You are his sister?"

Mary was speechless. Rabbi? They called him that? And he had disciples? So soon?

John carried the water jar clumsily, but as though it were no burden to him. Simon and Andrew stepped forward, bowing stiffly.

"Nay," the elder of these two said, "for all she looks so young, this is his mother, Mary. I would know her anywhere, even in a thicker fog than this, so often has the Master described her to me."

"You come from him!" Mary said. It was warm praise, the way she said it. They realized it was a great honor to be associates, and even friends, of Jesus. It was a proud boast to say, "Indeed we come from Jesus!" Yet they knew they were unworthy of such honor. They were unworthy to be greeted with such joy and esteem by this most beautiful and most gracious woman. John could not help blushing. Simon and Andrew looked abashed. They nodded again, stiffly.

"Aye," John said. "He bids us tell you he is well. He is suntanned to such a hue you might not know him. His long fast did him no harm. And neither the heat of the desert nor the cold of the desert nights had any lasting effect on him."

"Come in," Mary begged them. "I will rouse Salome and James and Joseph, his cousins, the children of Alpheus and Mary. Simon and Jude will be here soon. And others will come to make you welcome when they hear you have news of Jesus. He has been gone for years, it seems, though it has been only a few long weeks. And there has been much wonder in Nazareth about him."

The grotto was too crowded for comfort after all the relatives and neighbors had gathered. Mary opened the carpenter shop and the room where the ass had been stabled — as clean and shining now as the rest of the house. And she arranged cushions and pallets for the guests.

But scarce had the three men begun to tell about how John the Baptist had baptized Jesus, after arguing that Jesus should baptize him and not he Jesus, when someone knocked loudly on the door. Mary answered the knock, and found a boy on a donkey. She talked to him in whispers, and returned to her guests, picking up a wrap from a chest Joseph had made for her shortly after they were married.

"I am sorry," she said, "but I must go. There is a poor girl in Cana who has no one who can really help her. She is to be married early next week, and her mother is ill. I must go at once. There is much to do. The bridesmaids who must go out with the bride to meet the bridegroom! The bride's dress! The jewels she must have! I shall have to borrow them from the neighbors. The food that must be prepared. There are so many many things waiting to be done! I must go at once."

John shot up to his full height, and bowed to her.

"I will escort you," he said.

"Oh no," Mary protested. "It is not far. It is only in Cana. It will take but a day to walk. Do you all stay here and give your news to these, his people."

"Simon and Andrew will stay," John said quickly. "I will buy an ass in the village. The Rabbi's mother shall not walk. And I will be honored to accompany you."

"And I," shouted Peter in somewhat of an angry voice. "No

youngster will speak for me. I too will go with you. And my brother Andrew also."

John laughed and turned his shining face to all the listeners.

"The Rabbi Jesus turned this man into a rock," he said. "He changed his name to Peter, because Peter is as obstinate as a rock — and as easily moved. Once he sets himself for or against anything, there is no budging him."

"So now the idler is a Rabbi"? one of the oldest of the audience asked. "A Rabbi with disciples?"

It was Peter who silenced him.

"He is the Rabbi of rabbis," he said, his voice a challenge. "He is the Messiah. You do him little honor to call him 'idler.' No man is busier in the kingdom of heaven."

With a few quiet words, a smile, and a simple gesture, Mary banished every feeling of rancor in the crowded grotto and restored a measure of peace.

"Salome," she said, "will you stay here to greet Jesus when he comes, and to tell Him about the wedding in Cana?"

Such beauty flooded the girl's face that John was startled. Startled, yet not surprised. He knew how she felt.

"I — I won't mind," Salome said. "I won't mind at all."

"I'll stay too," said her brother James.

"And I," said Joseph and Simon and Jude.

"He should not be long in coming," John assured them. "He is with two other disciples now, Philip and Nathaniel. He has changed Nathaniel's name as well as Simon's. But Philip's and Andrew's and mine he has not changed. He is close to John the Baptist. He and the others preach to the people this side of the Jordan. And everywhere he goes, people flock to him as sheep to a shepherd. He is loved everywhere."

Mary was completing arrangements for the wedding dinner when Jesus arrived in Cana with Philip and Nathaniel, and those who had awaited him in Nazareth. She could hardly restrain herself from running to him and mothering him as though he were still a child. She could not, however, manage the joy that danced and leaped and turned somersaults in her heart. He was taller than she had remembered him, although she knew right well he had not grown a fraction of an inch. He was wearing the seamless robe she had made for Him, and a white linen head covering with broad purple stripes in it — a long veil, fastened around his head with a white and purple cord, which fell gracefully to his shoulders.

He still reminded her of Joseph. He walked the way Joseph had walked. He pronounced words the way Joseph had taught him to pronounce them. His eyes lit up with glory, even as Joseph's had, when he looked at her. Yet never had she seen such glory in Joseph's eyes as she saw now in the eyes of her Son, "the Rabbi Jesus."

There was no need to talk. There seldom was, when they looked at each other like that.

She went on with her work, after a few words of greeting. He would tell her all the details of the baptismal ceremony that Peter and Andrew and John had forgotten. She would wait until he had time to talk to her in private.

But it was not until late that evening that she had an opportunity to say anything to him. And then it was only about the wine. The chief steward had complained that he had served the last bottle of wine. . . . unless the bridegroom had a supply stored somewhere in the house. What a disgrace it would be to the young couple, now so very happy, if they would have to send away all these people! What guests would stay if there was no wine?

She made her way to where Jesus reclined with his disciples, and spoke to him softly.

"They have no wine," she said.

"Woman," Jesus answered — blue flames leaping from his

eyes to meet the blue flames in her own — "what is that to me, and to you? My hour has not yet come."

She almost laughed with the new happiness He gave her. That lovely name. Woman! The way he caressed it made her feel angelic ecstasy. And he was teasing her, as he had so often done when he was a child.

Imagine the Son of God pretending to be unconcerned at such a tragedy as menaced this household, he who once had told her his Father noted even the fall of a sparrow! Of course he would do something about the wine. And his hour really had come, although the Holy Ghost might not yet have told him so. She had only to speak to the Holy Ghost, her Spouse, and he would speak to the "Boy." She was so attuned to the will of God that, consciously or unconsciously, she could not help adjusting all her thoughts and actions to it.

Without hesitation she summoned the nearest waiters, and gestured toward her Son.

"Do whatever he tells you to do," she said. The problem was settled. She hurried off on some other pressing errand.

Jesus saw six tall waterpots standing against a wall. The water in them had been used to purify the hands of the guests. The vessels were empty.

"Fill them with water," Jesus bade the waiters. When they had done so, he ordered one to take a cup full of the contents of a pot and bring it to the chief steward. Then he turned to his disciples, resuming a story he had been telling them.

The chief steward tasted what was in the cup. Nathaniel, looking over Jesus' shoulder saw the pleasure in the steward's face, the amazement, and then the growing indignation. He knew something wonderful had happened. But what was it? Had the water really become wine?

He saw the steward go in search of the bridegroom. He followed. He heard the steward say: "Every other host gives his guests good wine first; and lesser vintages when they have become drunk enough not to know the difference. But you have kept the good wine until now."

Nathaniel sipped of the wine that had never known a vineyard or a cluster of black grapes. He had never tasted wine of such a quality, of such a flavor, or of such a fragrance.

The wine was served to the guests. They drank it without comment, unaware of its divine excellence. In that moment Nathaniel felt pity for all men who cheat themselves of pleasure by overindulging in pleasure.

The waiters sipped the wine, and knew that a miracle had happened. They sent the word racing through the world.

Lucifer was dismayed. He had used wine for many centuries to send souls to hell. Jesus used it to please his mother, to save his friends from embarrassment, and to proclaim himself the God-like Son of God!

"I will pay you back for this, O lordly Nazarene," the devil vowed. "I will pay you back in wine. In wine, and in dripping blood!"

CHAPTER XVI

As soon as it was light, Jesus departed from Cana with his disciples. His mother and some of his kindred accompanied him. As they walked along the shore of the Sea of Galilee, its waves splashing gently on the rocky beach, they encountered Zebedee with his two sons, John and James. They were in a boat, mending their nets. In a boat nearby were Simon, called Peter, and his brother Andrew.

Simon made the introductions; and Zebedee rocked land and sea with his shout of joy. He was standing up to his hips in water, and the net he held concealed him from the visitors, except for his head and beard. To Mary he seemed, at first, like a great, bronzed, wrinkled, bushy white head set on the pedestal of a long, stiff, shining white beard.

"Joseph's widow?" he roared. "Moon in the heavens! Heard Joseph talk about you for hours. Never bored me for a minute. Fifteen, twenty, no, thirty years or more ago. Met him in Jerusalem that day. Offered him a keg of fish. Wouldn't take it. Wanted to buy it. It was for a friend, he said. A gift! Said something I never forgot. 'The more bitter the sacrifice, the more blessed the gift!' Never forgot him either. Your Boy looks more like you than Joseph. But he's all man. Netted both my boys. Seen only one so far. Makes no difference. Other one's like a fish out of water, half dead, half alive. No good to me. Just waiting for the Rabbi."

He wiped his wet hands on his beard, as though it were a towel, and emerged dripping onto the sands, laughing at Jesus.

"Don't mind me, Master," he shouted. "I'm 'Thunderhead,' or just plain 'Thunder.' Born in a boat. In a storm. Had to out-thunder thunder to get attention. Still trying to get it. Giving you both these groupers. They're all gills and fins; but there's good meat on them. Ask their mother if you don't believe me. Bitter sacrifice, Rabbi. But — as your father would say — blessed gift. Breaks their mother's heart. Glad I'm not a woman. Stay overnight with us, all of you. Plenty room. Simon and the boys will take you to Bethsaida. I go fishing alone. Tell me one thing, Rabbi. What's your bait?"

"Your gift is blessed indeed," Jesus said. "I accept it. Keep your sons with you. I will come for them when I am ready."

Zebedee brushed his ears with the tail of his beard, whisking away two tiny clouds of flies. He bowed to Jesus and to Mary, got nimbly into his boat, and shoved hastily off. Mary thought he was wiping his eyes with his beard; but his back was turned. She could not be sure.

John and James jumped ashore, John almost tripping over his net. And both stood gazing with wonder and love at Mary.

"I have dreamed of this," John said. "Having you and Rabbi Jesus in our home."

"Joseph used to come here," James said, "when he was as old as John is now. He liked building and repairing boats. He lived with us once, father says."

"You will have his room," John said. "It looks out on the lake. You can see the shore, full of all kinds of flowers growing among the rocks. And there are so many beautiful stones there. Even bits of alabaster! And there's always the clean strong smell of seaweed!"

James pointed to the white top of a mountain rising far away, across the turquoise ripples of the lake.

"That's Mount Hermon," he said. "It is always beautiful."

"At sundown," John added, "it turns to all the colors of the rainbow. And even at night, when it is very dark, you can see it there, holding up the stars!"

They stayed in Bethsaida for a night and a day, then went to Capharnaum, where Simon and Andrew lived. And on the Sabbath, Jesus was invited to address the congregation in the synagogue.

"And they were astonished at his doctrine," St. Mark writes in his Gospel. "For he was teaching them as one having power, and not as the Scribes."

He was telling them how much God loved them, and why he loved them. And he was telling them why they should love God and each other.

It was torture for Lucifer and his imps.

"There was in their synagogue," St. Mark tells us, "a man with an unclean spirit; and he cried out, saying: 'What have we to do with thee, Jesus of Nazareth? Art thou come to destroy us? I know who thou art, the Holy One of God.'

"And Jesus threatened him, saying: 'Speak no more, and go out of the man.' And the unclean spirit, tearing him, and crying out with a loud voice, went out of him. And they were all amazed, insomuch that they questioned among themselves, saying: 'What thing is this? What is this new doctrine? For with power he commandeth even the unclean spirits, and they obey him.' And the fame of him was spread forthwith into all the country of Galilee."

Lucifer was once again close to being convinced that Jesus was the true Son of God. He did not drive out devils by prayer or fasting. He ordered them out by his own authority!

Jesus and his followers filed slowly out of the synagogue, and strolled, in silence, to the home of Simon and Andrew. People stared at them as they passed. When they reached the house they discovered that Simon's mother-in-law was ill.

"She's burning up with a fever," Simon said to Jesus. "Help her, Rabbi! My wife died of this same disease, last winter."

People nearby, hearing his words, and noting the anxiety in them, came closer. They entered the house. They saw Jesus take the woman's hand, lift her up, and cure her completely. They hurried away, some of them running hard, Sabbath or no Sabbath, to tell the news to friends and relatives miles away.

The patient sprang out of bed as soon as the divine Physician and his following had left the room, and helped Mary and Salome prepare and serve the dinner. The guests ate in comparative silence, for nearly everyone was wrapped in meditation. They were thinking either of the sermon about God and the kingdom of God; or about the cool matter-of-fact way Jesus had rescued the man from the devil; or about the simplicity of his method in curing the hostess.

No one was surprised to see great crowds gathering about the house toward sundown, some bringing sick friends or relatives with them. And when the Sabbath ended — when the rising moon had blotted and blotched the wet red and gold paint on the horizon — Jesus went out to attend them as doctor and priest, and as loving father and abiding friend.

Mary and the others watched while Jesus worked. Only his disciples went with him out of the house. They managed to put some sort of order in the crowds, to form a line of the sick and the crippled and the blind and the paralyzed and the possessed. Some of the patients lay on cots or pallets. Some lay on blankets. Some were stretched out on the pebbly beach, the waves approaching near to them and retreating hurriedly away. Frequently the disciples were called upon to lift a patient and carry him forward, pallet and all. And now and then they were forced to curb some ailing woman's impatience or to assure a man he would be cured as soon as possible.

Jesus worked without medicines, without any sort of surgical implements. He used only a word, a smile, a touch, a gesture, but even the worst of the patients rose and walked after he had touched them. Some of the blind leaped up, singing hysterically that they could see. Once in a while Jesus lifted a child from the ground, held him a moment close to his heart, then sent him running to his mother.

And every once in a while Jesus forced one or more devils out of a woman or a man — always bidding them to be silent. Their outcries might alarm those waiting to be cured. There was enough noise without the protests of exiled devils; for babies whimpered and screamed, little boys and girls sobbed and cried through fear, their elders moaned and groaned and cursed aloud, and called on Jesus — and on all the other sick — to hurry, hurry, hurry! Some who had been given back the use of their eyes or ears or arms or legs or tongues danced and sang and prayed. A few gave thanks aloud.

Jesus tended each one gently, swiftly, deftly, Mary noted. He looked at each patient with love, with pity, with a divine yearning for their happiness here and hereafter. He seemed to know, and to feel, the pain of all those he attended. He seemed also to know their weaknesses and their sins. He healed their souls, Mary thought, even as he healed their bodies.

He was at his Father's business. And he would work at it all night long, she knew, and perhaps well into the morning; for the more he cured, the more were brought to him. There were such crowds everywhere that the happy patients could scarcely pass through them. The newcomers made way reluctantly for them.

This would be his life from now on, Mary realized. This and preaching and teaching. He would go through all Israel, carrying his Father's love and care to all. He would be away from her often, for weeks or months at a time. She must expect this. She must resign herself. Nay, she must be glad that she could suffer so, through his absence.

Toward dawn, when the restless sun had begun to stir, the crowds thinned. Before it rose in its splendor, the last patient had gone joyfully away. Jesus stole out into the desert to talk to his Father in privacy. And there, after a time, his six disciples found him.

"There are new crowds about the house," Simon said, "and everybody wants you, the able-bodied as well as the sick."

"Let us go," Jesus said, rising. "And let us go into the neighboring towns and cities. I have come to preach to the people, to heal the sick, and to cast out devils. Follow me."

They went through the countryside without a good-bye to anyone. They ate what was thrust into their hands — sometimes seated around a great flat rock, sometimes alone and apart. They slept when and where they could. Sometimes they spent the night in ministering to the poor and wretched, and there was no time to sleep. When the Passover approached, however, Jesus sent the fishermen back to their nets and made his way to Jerusalem with Philip and Nathaniel — whom Jesus now called Bartholomew.

Lucifer had prepared the way. "There is a Man of Galilee," he spread the word, "who pretends to heal the sick with the laying-on of hands, and to cast out devils with a word. If he casts out devils, it is by the power of Beelzebub, the prince of devils. But, as you know, there really are no devils. The poor creatures that are said to be possessed by evil spirits merely believe they are possessed. So, in a sense, they are possessed. This man, this Jesus of Nazareth, takes advantage of them. He should be put away. He should be turned over to the Sanhedrin. He should be put to death."

Nobody knew Jesus when he entered the Temple with Philip and Bartholomew; but they saw he was someone of great importance and authority, for his eyes blazed with such an anger that men shivered and sought to escape his gaze.

He was angry at what he saw in the Court of the Gentiles, and with what he heard.

The holy place reeked with the smell of the cattle and sheep and goats and doves waiting to be sold and slaughtered. The beautiful floor was littered with the droppings of sheep and the dung of oxen. The air was filled with fat buzzing flies; and the floor with crawling vermin. Men selling and buying animals for sacrifice haggled and cursed and quarreled. The animals, even the most patient of them, made sad noises, calling to their mothers — or to their lambs and calves. Money changers, arrogant and greedy, counted coins in loud and blaspheming voices — and cheated as many as they could.

This in the house built to honor his Father, the most beautiful and ornate building in the world! Gold and marble everywhere — and everywhere filth and stench and avarice and lies!

All over Galilee, among the poorest of the poor, God was worshiped piously. Here, where holiness was to be expected, among the richest of the rich, among the priests and levites and doctors of the law, people worshiped Mammon and robbed the hundreds of thousands of pilgrims who had come to honor God.

Pieces of rope lay on the dirty floor. Wherever beasts are brought to market there are ropes. Jesus picked up a few lengths and made a scourge of them. Holding this in his right hand, he flung himself into an attack on those who had defiled the Temple, lashing right and left. Yet in spite of his holy wrath, he took care — it seemed to Lucifer — not to inflict any serious bodily injuries. He showed the fury of an avenging angel together with the concern of a human father. He wanted those sinners to recognize the enormity of their sin, and to be sorry for it, even while he punished them! Was it possible he loved those thieves and cheaters? Lucifer noted that Jesus did not lay a rope's end on any of the sellers of doves. He did not speak harshly to them. He bade them take the birds out of the Temple, and to keep them out. Nothing more than that.

The dealers, some of them powerful brutes and noted brawlers, ran in panic, slipping and sliding in the piles of dung, rising, falling, scrambling toward the gates, frightening the sheep and oxen so that they stampeded, bleating and bellowing, and rushed everywhere; colliding with one another, leaping over one another, fighting for freedom. The air was filled with a thousand frantic wings; and the floor was filled with thousands of spinning, circling, jingling, wheeling coins — and with scores of ragged little boys.

"My Father's house," Jesus shouted at the fleeing horde, "was meant to be a house of prayer. You have made it a den of thieves."

Lucifer began to doubt again. Jesus had been fearful in his anger. But he had not been Godlike. When the Most High was provoked, he did not make a mere scourge of ropes. He poured down fire and brimstone from flaming skies. He burned whole cities. He buried people alive. He led armies into ambush on land and in the sea and killed every man of them. He put fiery serpents on the earth, and plagues that brought death to thousands. He exploded mountains. He shook the land. He agitated oceans so that great fleets perished. If Jesus were the true Son of such a Father, how could he be so mild?

Maybe he meant what he had said about his Father's love for men, his Father's justice, and his Father's mercy. Maybe he was influencing his Father to temper justice with mercy — even to be more merciful than just! If the Most High were to listen to this Man, Lucifer thought, and to spread his divine mercy as a carpet for men to walk on with their dirty feet, it would mark the beginning of the end of the kingdom of hell on earth.

Lucifer would be helpless — unless he could induce men to reject God's mercy, to despise it, or to have no faith in it.

After a little time the chief priests came, the Pharisees, the Scribes, the doctors of the law, and the Sadducees. Unsmiling men who wanted an explanation from the Man with the scourge of ropes. They could not accuse him of any crime, for they knew the cattle and sheep should not have been permitted in the Temple, nor the dealers in animals and coins. Each one of them, Lucifer saw clearly, felt guilty — too guilty to look at Jesus squarely. They squinted red eyes at him. They made gestures to show their feelings.

But all they dared say was to ask by what authority he had acted.

Jesus looked at them sorrowfully. But his speech was almost gay.

"Destroy this Temple," he said, "and in three days I will raise it up."

That, he knew, would sound like a riddle to them or like sheer foolishness. He was speaking of his body; the real Temple of the Lord. He was thinking of his crucifixion, and of his resurrection on the third day.

Now they looked at him. And now they gave vent to the anger that churned in them. It had taken forty-six years to build this Temple, they told him. And he would raise it up in three days if it were destroyed? Bah!

Lucifer was sure that Jesus referred to himself when he spoke of the Temple; but the matter of the three days baffled him. If Jesus meant he would come back from the dead three days after Lucifer had destroyed him, he was wrong. Nobody ever came back from the tomb through his own power.

The devil was as pleased as a demon could be; for now the masters of Israel were on his side. It was they who profited most from the sale of animals and doves — especially Annas, the old high priest, and Caiphas, his son-in-law, who now had the title of high priest. They owned most of the beasts the pilgrims had to buy. They bought them cheap and sold them for ungodly sums. They also had an interest in the money changers' profits.

They would be happy when Lucifer told them how they might put this Man to death. Businessmen such as they did not scruple to take drastic measures when their business was endangered.

They were good at offering sacrifices, these priests. Let them sacrifice the Christ then — if indeed, he was the Christ — to his Father!

And what would the Father do to them? He would reward them suitably, Lucifer thought — which was a joke to be relished even in the bottomless pits of hell.

CHAPTER XVII

There was little encouragement for Jesus in the capital of his kingdom of sinners. There was little peace for him in its Temple, the house of his Father. The priests and levites, the Scribes and the Pharisees and the Sadducees, all scorned him. And, to the full extent of their power, they kept their followers from him. These proud men, these masters in Israel, hated and despised the common people, the workers and peasants. But the common people looked up to them with a blind faith and obeyed them.

Jerusalem, "the holy city," was a city of pride and malice. Its leaders believed neither in Moses nor in God. They believed only in themselves. Jesus was the light and the life of the world; but they preferred to walk in darkness and to remain inside the whited sepulchers of their own minds.

Jesus had come out of Galilee, with joy of the wedding at Cana, and his first public miracle, still singing in his veins. He had come as a bridegroom to claim his bride. He had been rebuffed, rejected, bitterly spurned. He had come with gifts of infinite love, infinite wisdom, infinite joy. He had been treated as an intruder, a most unwelcome guest, even as a suspected heretic and blasphemer. He had come as a sower of seed; and found the soil too flinty to let his seeds take hold and grow.

Many men had been attracted to him, through his preaching,

and through the fame of the miracles he had wrought; but they, he knew, were merely curious. One of the Pharisees, Nicodemus, however, did come to him. This was something of a victory, though the man came secretly, in the darkness of the night. He was afraid of what his friends might think or say if they saw him visiting Jesus. He came as stealthily as a deserter to the camp of the enemy. He knew Jesus had come from God as a teacher, and he wanted to ask questions. Jesus began by talking of baptism.

"Amen, amen I say to thee, unless a man be born again, he cannot see the kingdom of God." Nicodemus was amazed and puzzled, and a trifle indignant. Was Jesus toying with his intelligence? How could a man be born the second time? He did not know that Jesus was talking of the spirit. Nobody in Israel talked of the spirit. Jesus repeated the thought: "Amen, amen I say to thee, unless a man be born again of water and the Holy Ghost, he cannot enter the kingdom of God." He spoke further of the spirit, but Nicodemus interrupted with a question, "How can these things be done?" Jesus seemed shocked by this evidence of the man's spiritual poverty. "Art thou a master in Israel," he demanded, "and knowest not these things?"

Truly the blind were leading the blind in Israel. But they were blind because they wanted to be blind. They had eyes to see, but they would not look at anyone but themselves. They had ears to hear, but they listened only to their own human voices!

Then Jesus spoke to Nicodemus in these words: "No man hath ascended into heaven, but he that descended from heaven, the Son of man who is in heaven. And as Moses lifted up the serpent in the desert, so must the Son of man be lifted up; that whosoever believeth in him, may not perish, but may have life everlasting. For God so loved the world, as to give his only begotten Son, that whosoever believeth in him, may not perish, but may have life everlasting. For God sent not his Son into the world, to judge the world, but that the world may be saved by him. He that believeth in him is not judged. But he that doth not believe is already judged; because he believeth not in the name of the only begotten Son of God.

"And this is the judgment; because the light is come into the world, and men loved darkness rather than the light; for their works were evil. For every one that doth evil hateth the light, and cometh not to the light, that his works may be reproved. But he that doth truth cometh to the light, that his works may be made manifest, because they are done in God."

Nicodemus, like the other Pharisees, professed a religion that had no life in it — for where there is no spirit, there can be no life. But he was scholar enough to recognize Jesus' reference to Moses and the brazen serpent; and priest enough to meditate on it. The Lord had told Moses to make a serpent of brass and put it up on a pole for a sign, so that those who had been bitten by fiery serpents, might look on the sign and live. There must have been a crosspiece on that pole, else the sign might fall from the pole.

The Son of man, as Jesus called Himself, would also be placed on such a pole — the cross, which the Romans used in punishment of crime — that whosoever believed in him might not die in his sins, but have everlasting life!

Nicodemus could not have failed to understand most of the truths Jesus had given him. And he must have begun to live; for, sometime later, when Jesus was in danger, Nicodemus made a plea for him. It was a mild plea. But Nicodemus was a mild man. And this was most surely an indication of his concern and his love. It could also be a sign of his belief.

Jesus had been speaking of the "living water" he could give. He had so stirred the crowds who surged around him that he had alarmed the Pharisees and Scribes. They sent men to arrest him. What they would have done to him, nobody can say. But it was known that Caiphas, the high priest, had a prison deep below the entrance hall to his home, where a man could be kept indefinitely — for Rome would never learn of it.

"If anyone thirst let him come to me and drink." That was the cry that enraged the Pharisees and made them think of murder. Who did this impudent rascal think he was? God? "Let him come to me and drink. He who believes in me, as the Scripture says, 'From within him there shall flow rivers of living water.' "

They were doubly enraged when their police spies returned without the Prisoner, and with the excuse that they had been so spellbound by Jesus they had forgotten their errand.

"Have you also been led astray?" one of the priests shouted, ready to tear both his garments and his flesh. "Why do you believe in him? Are you wiser than we are? Do you know of any ruler who believes in him? Or any Pharisee? Of course not! Only those cursed ones who do not know the Law believe in him."

It was then Nichodemus found sufficient courage to speak up. "Doth our law judge any man unless it first hear him and know what he doth?" His fellow Pharisees could have crushed him. "Are you also a Galilean?" they asked. "Search the Scriptures and see that out of Galilee arises no prophet."

Jesus loved and hated the Pharisees, as a father loves and hates his wicked, headstrong, hell-bound sons. He was sorry to leave them, since he could not help them. But he must go north.

He stopped for a time near Salem, where John was baptizing; and this caused some of John's disciples to complain of Jesus and "his competition." John rebuked them gently. "A man cannot receive anything unless it be given him from heaven. He that hath the bride is the bridegroom. But the friend of the bridegroom rejoices when he hears the bridegroom's voice. Therefore my heart is filled with joy."

The prophets had said the Messiah would be the bridegroom of Israel, and of all the world. John wanted his disciples to realize that Jesus was that bridegroom; and that he, John, was happy because, as the friend of the bridegroom, he had, after the custom of the Jews, arranged the wedding between Jesus and the world.

And, in order that his hearers might realize Jesus was **God**, and the Son of God, he added: "He must increase, but I must decrease. He that comes from above is above all. He that is of the earth is earthly, and of the earth he speaks. He who is sent by God speaks the words of God. The Father loves the Son, and has given all things into his hand. He who believes in the Son has life everlasting. He who does not believe shall not see life. But the wrath of God will remain upon him."

It was pleasant in and around Salem. The soil was rich enough to please the Sower of seeds. Philip and Bartholomew baptized many people. But a divine impatience was calling Jesus further north. And he coud not resist its urging.

It was a woman who summoned him. A beautiful, seductive, intelligent, restless, world-worn, love-hungry, disillusioned idealist. A woman who was the opposite of Nicodemus. She had abundant life, but no religion. She knew nothing of theology and ritual and respectability. She made no show of virtue. She did not fast, nor did she pray in public. The law of Moses never wooed or worried her. She was not timid; she was bold. She was a sinner, and she acknowledged it. And she could be a saint, for she contained much love!

She was a soul worth walking miles for; and Jesus walked those miles so rapidly his disciples had trouble keeping up with him. When he reached his goal, the shade of the trees near Jacob's well, it was noon. He sent his friends into the nearby town of Sichar, so they could buy provisions — and so he could be alone with the woman.

She had a rendezvous with God, but didn't know it. She came to the well at this hour because there would be no little snips of girls looking at her in that silly way they had; nor any of their elders who thought themselves so righteous and so pure. She could do without them. She could do without all other women. And without men too, if anyone should ask her. To her, one man was as vicious and stupid and hopeless as another. They were clods. And love was a stranger to them.

She had once believed that someday she would find a man worth a woman's love, a man worth working for, worth suffering for, worth fighting for, worth dying for. But now she was sure there was no such man. Now she believed love was a blossom without roots. It withered and died in a night. It had to be thrown away, like a weed.

She saw the Man waiting at the well, and came toward him with provoking slowness, unconsciously moving her shapely hips. He was a Jew. But magnificent! And there was an air of distinction about him. And a sense of tremendous power. He was watching her. She felt ridiculous. What could such a man want of her?

He wanted a drink of water! She was surprised only because he had spoken to her and had asked a favor. Men did not talk to women in any public place. And a Jew did not talk to a Samaritan, especially a Samaritan woman. The Jews regarded the Samaritans as heretics and schismatics; and the Samaritans hated and feared the Jews.

This Man was apparently above all these petty and hateful rules and regulations. He made his own rules! She began to feel at ease. She asked a few questions; and shivered delightedly as she saw his eyes catch fire. What a breathtaking Man he was!

He surprised her further by saying that if she knew who it was that asked her for a drink, perhaps she would have asked the gift of him, and he would have given her living water.

Somehow she knew what he meant by living water. He meant love such as she had dreamed of in wretched moments. There was something like love even now in his eyes. She could not be mistaken. She knew love when she saw it. But this was a different kind of love, one she had never known. This was a love that could not be sullied nor spoiled in any way, that never could be less than what it was; that had only begun to grow!

Yet even as she savored the truth, she denied it. There was no use fooling herself. It would only make life harder. The Man was speaking of the living water in the well. Jacob's well. It was a thousand years old, or more, so far as she knew; yet it was still alive. Jacob had provided it. Was the Stranger greater than Jacob? Did he have water with more life in it?

"Whosoever drinks of this water will thirst again," Jesus said. "But he who drinks of the water I give him, shall not thirst for ever. The water shall become a fountain in him, springing up into life everlasting."

She had been right at first. He did mean love, everlasting love.

"Sir," she begged, "give me this water that I may not thirst, nor come here again to draw water from this well." If she could have love, and never go back to any man again . . . !

"Go call your husband," Jesus said, "and come back with him."

"I have no husband," she said. She felt trapped. And she felt shamed. She had been given a taste of heaven, and it had been snatched away from her by the Man who showed it to her. Because she was not worthy of it!

"You have answered well," Jesus said, "telling me you have no husband. You have had five; and the man you live with now is not your husband." She looked at him closely. He was not condemning her! His eyes told her he understood, sympathized, pitied, forgave. He was a prophet! How did a woman talk to a prophet? What did one say to him? Something about worshiping

God, perhaps, "Our fathers adored God on this mountain," she said, "and you say he should be adored only in Jerusalem." Why did he not blast her? How was it that she could stand in the presence of such a Man — feeling the vilest of sinners, yet not wanting to be anywhere else in the world?

"Woman," Jesus said — she took new heart at the way he said that word — "the time will come when God will be adored neither in Jerusalem nor here on Mount Garizim. You adore that which you know not; we adore that which we know, for salvation is of the Jews. The hour approaches when the faithful will adore in spirit and in truth. God is a Spirit, and they who adore him must adore in spirit and in truth."

She waited, loving the music of his voice, the wonder of his words. But he seemed to have said all he had to say. That must not be! She must hold him a little longer. Perhaps if she talked about the Messiah, he might stay a little longer. "When the Messiah comes," she ventured, "he will tell us everything we need to know."

"I am he," Jesus said, revealing his secret for the first time. "I who am speaking to you, am the Messiah."

She knew he spoke the truth. She knew it by his eyes, and by the fountain of living water that had sprung up within her. She had been miraculously cleansed in body and soul; and she would have flung herself at the Savior's feet in love and gratitude and adoration, had not the disciples come in sight, burdened with the food they had bought in Sichar. She hurried away, leaving her waterpot behind her. The noon heat was pitiless, but she ran as though there were no burning sun above her, and as though she were a little girl. She was going to tell all her friends she had met the Messiah, the Christ, who had told her all about herself. She had gone to confession to him, and he had not scolded her at all. He had washed her with the living water of his love. She would be clean forevermore, and forevermore she would be happy. "Come and see the Christ!" she cried again and again. "Come and see the Christ!"

Philip and Bartholomew pretended not to have seen anything amiss. They approached Jesus solemnly, holding out food to him. But he was not hungry. He refused their offerings. "I have meat to eat which you know not," he said. "My meat is to do the will of him who sent me, that I may perfect his work."

He knelt in prayer, thanking his Father for the soul he had gained. The sinful Samaritan had become the first lay apostle of his kingdom; and she would bring him others. Philip and Bartholomew squatted in the dust, wishing Jesus had chosen a spot in the shade, wishing the place weren't so silent, so dead. They munched their food as quietly as they could, until Philip stirred and shot upright, knowing a queer sort of fear. "Look, Master," he said. "People rushing toward us!"

Jesus rose, smiling. "Do you not say there are four months between sowing and reaping?" he asked. "Lo, a few moments ago I planted one small seed. Now, behold, lift up your eyes and see! The fields are already white, and ready for the harvest. One man sows. Another reaps. The fruit is gathered into life everlasting. And both Sower and reaper may rejoice together. I send you to reap what you did not sow, and to harvest the fruit of the Sower's toil."

Here, at Jacob's well, far from Jerusalem, countless Samaritans declared that Jesus was indeed "the Savior of the world."

CHAPTER XVIII

From Samaria Jesus returned to Galilee, repeating everywhere the words of the Baptist, "Repent, for the kingdom of God is at hand," and adding words of his own; words never uttered before; words that seared hearts and consciences, stimulated minds, and strengthened the wills of sinful men; words that built a new world and gave it life and meaning.

To some he was the walking volcano of the Lord, in constant eruption. His head was in the clouds. Heavenly fire shone in his eyes. Great streams of lava issued from his lips, frightening some, warming others, setting souls afire — or hardening them beyond all former hardness. Aye, he was a volcano. To others he was a shining white cloud beckoning to all the children of God by day, and leading them in the path to heaven. And he was a pillar of fire and smoke by night — the one sure guide to those lost in the dark. He was the humblest of men, for he had time for everybody, no matter how unimportant. And he was the wisest, the kindest, the most kingly, the most powerful, the most loved and hated.

He was welcomed everywhere — until he reached the town of Nazareth, where he had spent most of his life. Unwieldy crowds had beset him wherever he appeared. Children surrounded him, held him, adored him. Men and women shouted

Hosannas to him, hemmed him in, begged favors of him, showered him with thanks. Youth offered itself to him in unparalleled generosity.

But there was little excitement in Nazareth when he came home. His old friends and neighbors had heard many stories about him, some good, some bad. Most of the tales were difficult to believe. They looked at him critically. He didn't seem to have changed. Even his clothes were the same. True, he had discarded the curly wood shavings that once hung from his ears to advertise the fact he was a carpenter. And he no longer had the fragrant scent of wood about him — pine or oak or sandalwood or cedar. But he was the same Man, the son of Joseph — the dreamer.

Now He was a rabbi, with disciples, an orator, even a prophet! How had he become so famous overnight? Who had taught him to speak so well? Who had trained him in all those tricks — like making the blind see? Why had he come home? To make other Nazarenes jealous? Was he going to reopen the carpenter shop, marry a local girl, and settle down to live, as normal, respectable, hard-working, stay-at-home people were supposed to live? Or was he going to stay just long enough to "put on a show"? Maybe he would change Nazareth's water into wine. That would be a fine trick to learn, but he probably wouldn't tell anybody how he did it. A man could get rich making wine that way.

Some said he was already rich through his preaching and his magic; and they wondered if he wasn't saving his money for a war chest. What he meant to do, they said, was to raise an army. That would take plenty of money. Once he had his army, he would crush Rome and establish his own kingdom. He would make himself king of the world, if he could. Imagine that for Joseph's Son! He actually expected to carve up the world as if it were nothing more than a piece of wood! He wasn't going to get any recruits in Nazareth, these men said. Folks there knew when they were well off.

Some of his kindred gave him a lukewarm reception. He had endangered himself, and them, they reminded him, by angering the Pharisees and Scribes, speaking his mind so boldly everywhere, and attracting so much attention with his outlandish words and ways. They hoped he would stay out of danger, at least in Nazareth. It was his visit to the synagogue that gave Nazareth the worst day in its history.

When he stood up to read, the book of Isaias was given him. And immediately Lucifer — who had followed a number of friends into the Holy place — was on the alert for trouble. Isaias! Must he haunt the devil forever?

Jesus unrolled the book. "The spirit of the Lord is upon me, wherefore he hath anointed me to preach the gospel to the poor, he hath sent me to heal the contrite of heart; to preach deliverance to the captives, give sight to the blind, to set at liberty them that are bruised, to preach the acceptable year of the Lord, and the day of reward." He rerolled the book and handed it back. He sat down and looked at his friends and neighbors, his face giving no sign of the storm he was about to loose.

This day, he told them, Scripture had been fulfilled by his coming here — thus inferring that he was the anointed of the Lord, the Messiah sent to preach, to heal, to free the captives, and to redeem the world! He told them what was in their hearts. They wanted him to show them the miracles he had wrought in Capharnaum; to prove himself. They were saying, "Physician, heal thyself." He told them he wasn't going to do what they expected.

He said to them: "A prophet is not without honor except in his own country, and among his own kindred, and in his own house." And he gave them two examples. When Elias was in need of food and shelter, and wanted protection from a wicked king, he was helped by a widow in Sarepta, in Sidon. She honored the prophet Israel had dishonored and abandoned. When Eliseus walked the earth there were many lepers in the land, but the only one who honored him by asking for a cure was the Syrian general, Naaman.

Jesus might eventually have made his old friends ashamed of their lack of faith in him; but Lucifer succeeded in stirring up their envy and their hatred.

"When this man walks the streets," he whispered, "his feet collect as much filth and corruption as your own. When he works, he sweats, as you do. His hands are as defiled as yours, for he touches many unclean things, as you do. When he is hungry he swallows down his food, as you do — though he has more to eat than you have, and it is better food. When he is thirsty he drinks, as you do. But his wine is costlier than yours. When he sleeps, he snores, as you do. He is a man, as you are. You know him well. He is Joseph's son. Yet now he would have you believe he is your God! He wants you to bend the knee to him, and knock the forehead against the dirt on which he stands. He wants you to make him your king; to pay him tithes — and more than tithes. Yet he despises you. He tells you, to your faces, that you are lower than the gentiles! You, the children of Abraham! You, the elect of Jahweh! How long will you sit here quietly and let him debase you, and your wives and children? How long will you let him blaspheme against your God?"

In Capharnaum, when Jesus made his first talk in the synagogue, a man possessed by a devil had interrupted him. He drove the devil away and healed the man. Here in Nazareth the devil went into every man listening to Jesus. They leaped up and rushed at him. They shouted, spat, cursed, tore their garments, and menaced him with their fists. They hemmed him in with their bodies, forced him out of the synagogue, up a narrow, slanting filthy street, and up the side of a hill that overlooked the town. And he did not cast out one devil!

It was a moment of triumph for the prince of evil. The Nazarene's own people were going to get rid of him! A nice ironic twist! A story with hell's own by-line. They were going to murder him while his mother and other relatives looked on, helpless to save him!

Up, up, up, the Nazarenes forced their victim. They crept up the hill like a dirty and noisy flood, Lucifer thought, the many colors of their robes adding a hellish confusion to the scene.

Jesus led the way, calmly, walking easily, his body erect. He could be readily distinguished from those who followed him — the savage waves lapping at his heels. He was dressed in a white robe, and he wore his white prayer cloak with the purple stripes in it, and his purple-and-white-striped head covering. His ex-friends made a semicircle behind him. They panted as they climbed. They yelled insults. They cried, "Kill him, kill him, kill him!" They stooped to pick up heavy rocks, stout sticks, handfuls of gravel or sand, or clumps of earth. It was not enough to throw him off the cliff onto the rocks below. They wanted first to smash his face, to spatter the earth with his blood, to bury him under dirt and rubble and sticks and stones and their own torn and dirtied clothing.

Lucifer puffed himself up to an enormous size as he watched the spectacle. Yet, glancing at Mary, who stood at the foot of the hill with her kindred, he shrank a little. She was not frightened. Her face was serene. She was comforting the young men and women. She was restraining them. They wanted to attack the mob and rescue Jesus! She was forbidding them! What did that mean?

When Jesus came close to the edge of the cliff, he turned and looked at the men around him, neighbors turned into wild beasts by the black magic of the devil. They glared at him, snarling, frothing at the mouth, saliva dribbling into their beards, faces streaked with sweat and grime and spittle, teeth bared, eyes aflame with malice.

No man touched him. No spittle reached him. No stone or stick or clump of earth came anywhere near him.

He looked at them without a trace of anger or of fear. There was only a divine compassion in his eyes. They shifted uneasily. They were silent. Jesus lifted his head, as though to study the unhurrying white clouds above him. Then he walked back down the hillside to his mother!

Lucifer remembered how it was when God made a passage through the Red Sea for Moses and his unhappy flock. The waves surged high on either side of that path. They were calm, and stationary, but they were flecked with foam and froth, like the faces of these men. They stood straight, yet their waters boiled with all the filth brought up from the bottom of the sea. It was like that now. The waves of men bent on murder had parted before the Son of man, made a path for Him. They had stood straight and unyielding, yet they boiled with sediment dredged from the depths.

When Jesus had passed through, the waves came together again as mysteriously, and as violently, as they had opened!

Lucifer, as awed and humbled and shaken as any of the Nazarenes, was, unlike them, inspired with new viciousness and courage. He made plans for total war. He could make use of these poor dupes, once they became their own knavish selves again. There was a streak of good rich hate in them, and a layer of real jealousy. He would have the Pharisees and Scribes till that soil. Those men had known Jesus since he was a child. They could tell a thousand stories about him — and each story might be made into a scandal Lucifer could use.

But this was a minor detail in his campaign. He must alert his friends in every city and town and hamlet in Israel, and see that they were prepared for battle. He had a great army at his disposal. He must assemble it and ready it for action.

First of all he must get rid of John the Baptist. He must show Jesus the prophet's head resting on a platter, blood dripping from it like red wine — that wine Jesus had blessed at Cana. He visited Herod Antipas, the tetrarch of Galilee, and whispered to him about John. And he visited Herodias, Herod's niece, sister-in-law, mistress, and wife. John was arrested and shut up in a dungeon. Then Lucifer began to work in earnest.

Jesus, after he had lodged his mother and his cousins in a house in Capharnaum, also set about the business of putting an army in the field. He began on the shore of the Lake of Tiberias — the sea of Galilee.

As he walked toward Bethsaida, hundreds of men and women and children flocked to him, pressed about him, pulled at his robe, and at the tassels that hung to his ankles. They followed him closely, lovingly, praying to him, asking favors of him. They said his name over and over and over.

Two ships were drawn up on the beach, and four men were washing their nets. Jesus knew the men. He greeted them with a warm smile, got into the nearer boat, and asked Simon Peter to shove it out into the water, so he might more easily talk to the people. When he had finished speaking, he bade Peter cast the nets into deeper water. That seemed a silly thing to Peter. He and Andrew and the sons of Zebedee had toiled all night and hadn't even smelled a fish. But he obeyed, without comment.

As soon as the nets were lowered they were filled. Peter and Andrew almost fell overboard trying to haul in their heavy catch. The nets broke with the strain. Frantic signals brought John and James to the rescue, and both ships were so filled with fish they were almost swamped!

This was too much for Simon Peter. He threw himself at his

Master's feet, heedless of the fish that squirmed and struggled and twitched beneath him, and cried out, "Depart from me, O Lord, for I am a sinful man!"

But Jesus had no intention of departing from any sinner — especially Peter.

Zebedee was waiting at Bethsaida. At first he looked like a little man waving a handkerchief. When the boats were closer, he became a tall man whose snow-white beard was fluttering in the breeze. "Moon in heaven," he roared. "If those ships leaked water like they leak fish, you would have drowned out there." He bowed to Jesus. "But you are fishing for my two minnows today," he guessed. "I knew it when I saw you. Aye. I knew it. Their mother will take it hard."

They went away, the four fishermen, without a word, without taking anything with them but the clothes they wore. They left the boats, the nets, the silver treasure of fish, their homes, their families and friends. They followed Jesus and the other disciples, Philip and Bartholomew. And they did not look back.

Zebedee watched them a long time, feeling old and useless, and strangely tired. He stooped, brushed several pounds of fish off the prow of his boat, and sat there a long time, feet in the water, hands on his beard. So many young men and boys were going to Jesus, with nothing but dreams in their pockets. They offered themselves for the strangest and greatest adventure the world had ever heard of, Zebedee thought. What would come of it? No other man had ever recruited an army in this fashion. It would be absolutely crazy, if Heaven hadn't something to do with it. Jesus looks at a man and says "Follow me!" The man gets up and follows him. He leaves the plow in the furrow, if he be in the field when he hears the call. If he look back, he is not worthy. He does not tarry because his father has died. He steps across the old man's corpse and follows his Lord, leaving the dead to bury the dead. He does not stop to say good-bye to his parents, to his sweetheart or his wife and children, or to his friends.

"If any man come to me and hate not his father and mother and wife and children, and brethren, and sisters, yea and his own life also, he cannot be my disciple!" Hard words, these; and hard to understand. But the meaning is clearer for the hardness. What could those men expect, leaving everything — including their dead and their aging fathers — to follow the living Lord? Poverty. Privations. Unending toil. Persecutions. A cross to carry. A frightful death to die. Yet the young men did not hesitate to give themselves to him, with their hopes and ambitions, and their holy trust. And they accepted, joyfully, the only rewards he promised.

Zebedee sighed deeply. He had seen Jesus many times, and had heard him speak. He would have followed him as eagerly as his sons, had he been young enough. But all he could do he had done. He went slowly toward his home, giving no thought whatever to the miraculous draft of fishes. He had to tell his wife, and let her weep her fill.

CHAPTER XIX

Simon Peter was one of those who looked upon Jesus as the holiest of holy prophets, whom a sinner must approach in fear and trembling. Jesus, who had come to rescue sinners, and who had an abiding love for them, was not entirely pleased with Peter's attitude. He wanted the man to love him perfectly, and perfect love casts out fear. To bring the fisherman closer to him, he arranged a private miracle for him; one that was as divinely amusing as it was baffling.

They were in Capharnaum. One of the men who collected the Temple taxes had looked, with something of a sneer, at Peter, and asked if his Master did not intend to pay the tax. Peter's impulse was to strike the man for such blasphemous impudence. No man should sneer when he spoke of Jesus. But he controlled himself.

"Of course," he said. He merely scowled at the man, and hurried to find Jesus and ask what he should do. He felt somewhat guilty. How had he dared answer for Jesus, when he had no idea of Jesus' feeling about the tax?

Jesus met Peter with a strange and mysterious smile. And he asked a question that Peter mistook for a riddle.

"From whom do the kings of earth demand tribute or customs dues? From their children or from others?"

"From others," Peter said.

"Then the children are exempt," Jesus remarked.

Abruptly Peter knew what the Lord was talking about. He was saying that he and Peter were children of God, and therefore not obliged to pay the Temple tax! He had bracketed himself with Peter, the wretched sinner! Such love as he had never known before took hold of Peter's heart and squeezed it.

"But," Jesus added — and now there was a gleam in his eyes that made Peter think of a mischievous boy planning a silly prank to play on one of his too-solemn professors — "lest we scandalize some people, let us pay the tax."

It was astonishing to think of Jesus, the Messiah, as a man with a sense of humor. Yet that's what He was — at least at the moment. Peter waited impatiently for the words of explanation he expected. But Jesus did not explain. Not exactly.

"Go to the sea," he said. "Take your rod. And hook a fish."

"One fish?"

Peter forgot this was some sort of joke. It wasn't possible to sell a fish, even a big one, for the money needed. Maybe the Rabbi didn't mean to sell the fish, though. What then? Was he going to have it cooked for the tax collector — and serve it as a sort of gift? No. He most certainly was not. Jesus never bribed anybody, even his disciples. He told them what to do, and they did it. Peter felt as he had the day Jesus told him to strike out for the deep and cast the nets. It might be a silly order; but it was an order. He would obey.

The smile on Jesus' face warmed Peter. "One fish. The first you catch. Open its mouth and you will find a silver coin, a Greek stater. That will pay for you and me."

Peter went to the seashore without hesitation and without the least doubt. He knew he would catch a fish. He knew it would have a coin in its mouth. Jesus had said so. And Jesus was not the Man to send anyone on a fool's errand. He caught a pike without any trouble. It wasn't a particularly big one. But it had the stater in its mouth. It had probably been waiting there for him, swimming around and around until he should keep the rendezvous arranged by Jesus. It had probably refused the bait offered by less fortunate fishermen; saving its money for Peter.

Only a man in a lighthearted mood could think of such a nice way of entertaining a friend — and at the same time such an original way of earning money. But only a man endowed with the power of almighty God could have made the thought come alive. "If we needed two staters," Peter thought, "that same fish would have had them."

He noticed the tax collector looked a little less hostile when he took the coin and a little more human.

"So you're a fisherman," the man said.

"How did you know?" Peter demanded, instantly on the defensive.

"The coin smells like fish," the other answered. He eyed Peter with something like respect, and Peter was glad he hadn't said what was in his mind. The man meant well. "You must be a good fisherman," he observed, "or a lucky one. For there's seldom any money in fish."

Peter laughed so hard the man thought he had said something funny. He laughed with Peter. "I could tell you a story," Peter said, "but the trouble with fish stories is that nobody believes them. Suppose I told you a fish paid me that stater to save his life; and that I threw him back into the sea when I took his money!" He walked away laughing.

Peter liked this man, yet felt shame at acknowledging it; for tax collectors, whether they worked for Rome or for the Temple were not fit associates for any self-respecting Jew. Rome had sold its rights to tax the people. Rich and noble and greedy men had bought the taxing concession. They raised the rates so they could have a profit after paying their Roman friends. To

gather these taxes they hired unscrupulous men who did not
stop at cheating the rich and the moderately wealthy, but also
gouged the last coppers out of the poor and the sick and the
dying. They charged more than their employers expected — thus
enriching themselves. The Pharisees and the other masters in
Israel felt defiled if the shadow of a publican fell upon them.
They felt only a little less sullied by the presence of the Temple
collectors — for these also had a tendency to overcharge, to
embezzle, and to cheat.

Later Peter decided that he was wrong about publicans of all
sorts. That was after Jesus had seen the publican, Levi, and had
beckoned to him. "Follow me," Jesus said. And Levi got up, left
everything, and followed him. If a publican was good enough
for Jesus, he was good enough for Peter. And, he added to himself, good enough for the rest of them, including the sons of
"Thunder." They had better accept Levi as Peter did. They had
better keep their mouths shut too. He did not have the least
scruple — he was proud to think — about accompanying Jesus
to a feast Levi provided in his home. This in spite of the fact
that he knew Levi had invited many of his publican friends.

Galilee shuddered when it learned Jesus had not only accepted
a publican as a disciple, but had even gone to his house to dine
with him and other publicans. A group of lordly Pharisees, and
some of the followers of John the Baptist, boldly strode into the
house to see if the tale was true. In the presence of Peter and
others, the Pharisees made bitter remarks. Before Peter could
cool his anger sufficiently to answer the arrogant intruders, Jesus
spoke. He said that healthy people had no need of a doctor,
whereas sick people did. He was a doctor. He had come to heal
the sinners, the sick; not the just.

He told them: "Go and learn what this means: 'I desire mercy
and not sacrifice.'"

One of the followers of John the Baptist took up the insulting questions. "Why do we and the Pharisees fast, while your disciples eat, drink, and enjoy themselves?"

Jesus reminded him of John's remarks about the "bridegroom."

"Can the children of the bridegroom mourn, so long as the bridegroom is with them? The day will come when the bridegroom will be taken from them. Then they shall fast."

John's disciple flushed with embarrassment, remembering how his master had declared Jesus was the very Son of God, and shook with helpless anger because, by so few words, this friend of publicans and sinners had confounded him.

Jesus then spoke words they could not understand. They wanted to hurry away, these men who had come to condemn him publicly, but they could not help staying until he had finished.

"Nobody," he said, "puts a patch from a new garment on an old one. It would not match. It would ruin the new garment. And it would make the old one look ridiculous. Nobody puts new wine into old wineskins. That would be to burst the skins and spill the wine. New wines must be put into fresh skins."

He had a new wine, the heady wine of love, and he meant to put it into a new container. But this was not the time to talk frankly about it.

"And no man, after drinking old wine," he added, "calls immediately for a new vintage. He thinks the old is better."

When Jesus had given them leave, the invaders withdrew in sullen silence. Jesus reclined again. Another course was served. The feast continued. It was, up to this time, the happiest day in the life of the publican Levi, who would be renamed Matthew, and who would be numbered among the Apostles and also among the four Evangelists.

Jesus had recruited a great number of disciples before he sent the wine of love into the towns and cities of Galilee. He had

twelve Apostles. And he had seventy-two others he could depend
upon. He dispatched them in pairs, to bring God's love to the
people; and to bring the people's love of God back to him.

They were all rugged men, these chosen ones. They had to be,
for the work to which Jesus had called them would tax their
strength to the utmost. They were simple men. They must trust
solely in God. They must take nothing with them on their travels
through the country, "neither staff, nor wallet, nor bread, nor
money," nor extra clothing. They must preach the Gospel everywhere: "The kingdom of God is at hand." And they must live
on the Gospel — for the laborer was worthy of his hire.

"I send you as lambs into the midst of wolves," he said to
them. "Therefore be as wise as serpents and as simple as doves.
But beware of men; for they will deliver you up, and they will
scourge you. You will be hated by all men for my name's sake.
The disciple is not above the master, nor the servant above his
lord. Fear not them that kill the body, but him that can send
both body and soul to hell. Are not two sparrows sold for a
farthing? Yet not one of them falls to the ground without your
Father's knowledge. Fear not, therefore; you are better than
many sparrows."

He gave them power to cast out devils, to cure the sick, to
raise the dead, and to give his peace to men of good will. "Everyone who confesses me before men," he said, "I will confess
before my Father who is in heaven. But he that shall deny me
before men I will deny him before my Father. Who receives you
receives me. Who receives me, receives him who sent me. If a
town refuse to receive you, shake off its dust and leave it. It
will be more tolerable for the land of Sodom and Gomorrha in
the day of judgment than for that city. Woe to you, Corozain!
Woe to you, Bethsaida! For if in Tyre and Sidon the miracles
had been worked that were worked in you, they would have
repented long ago in sackcloth and ashes. And you, Caphar-

naum, shall you be exalted to heaven? You shall be thrust down to hell!"

The harvest was great, he reminded them, but the laborers were few. He asked them to pray "the Lord of the harvest" to send more laborers to help them. Laborers were needed, indeed; but Jesus would not accept all those who applied. A Scribe volunteered to follow him; but Jesus saw he was soft, unaware of the toil and the strain and the danger of being a disciple, and utterly unfit for the work.

"The foxes have holes," he said to this man, "and the birds have nests. But the Son of man has nowhere to lay his head." The Scribe walked quickly away. He had to have something better than a fox hole. Another man Jesus refused was an able-bodied youth filled with goodwill. He had lived a good life. All he had to do now, Jesus said, was to sell what he had, give the money to the poor, "and come follow me." This man walked away slowly. He wanted to follow Jesus, but he was very rich. He couldn't afford to be a disciple, he thought. Think of giving up all that money so he might be a beggar and follow a Beggar!

Lucifer was not impressed with the men Jesus had chosen. They were just average. They could be tempted, but some were a little too tough for the devil's liking. John, for instance, was even tougher than he looked. Lucifer began to hate the sight of him. He was so much in love with Jesus, and with Mary, the mother of Jesus, that he was unendurable. He not only resisted temptations, he fought back. His brother was like him, but not nearly so intense. Peter was a queer one too. He was a stout lover of his Master, but a man of indecision. He could be handled easily when the time came. The easiest of all, Lucifer discovered, was Judas Iscariot.

Lucifer could not help noting, however, that these ordinary men were attracting many people, and leading them away from hell. That must be stopped, of course, in time. Right now it was helping the devil; for it was stiffening the Pharisees and Scribes in their opposition to Jesus. And Jesus himself, was increasing his enemies among the powerful ones in Israel by his denunciations.

Never had a man been so bitter as Jesus was in condemning the Pharisees. Never had any man called them such names. The Nazarene, for all his gentleness and kindness, was a master of insult and reproach. The Pharisees, he told great crowds of humble Galileans, were hypocrites. They dressed for show, to be admired. They wanted the first places at feasts, the first chairs in the synagogues. They wanted to be greeted in the market-places and to be called rabbi. They were blind men leading the blind. They were worse, for they kept the people out of the door to the kingdom of heaven. They did not want to enter that kingdom; but they stood in its doorway and blocked it. They prayed long prayers, to get attention; yet they devoured the houses of widows; and they made their proselytes children of hell.

They were keen for tithing the people, but were not concerned about right judgment, mercy, or faith. They were men who strained at a gnat and swallowed a camel. They were whited sepulchers — whitewashed tombs that looked beautiful from outside, but were filled with dead men's bones and corruption. They were always washing the outside of the cup, never the inside.

And, like John the Baptist, He called them a brood of vipers, and asked how they were to escape the judgment of hell.

And the Scribes? Woe to them, Jesus said, for they loaded men with unbearable burdens, and did nothing to help them. Woe to them also because they approved of the deeds of their fathers who had killed the prophets.

It was evident to Lucifer that even when he was denouncing the Pharisees and Scribes, Jesus was warning them. He was worried about them. He wanted to save them from hell. He probably loved them as much as he loved other sinners; but felt he must not show them his love, lest it encourage them to stay in their sinful ways.

Lucifer was confirmed in this opinion on the day when Jesus, talking to a multitude of simple people, suddenly directed an appeal to a group of Pharisees — men standing proudly apart from the vulgar throng, listening with impassive faces and un-hearing ears. "Jerusalem, Jerusalem," Jesus cried, "thou that killeth the prophets and them that are sent unto thee, how often would I have gathered together thy children, as the hen doth gather her chickens under her wings; and thou wouldst not!"

The love and the hate and the fear throbbing in that outcry made the devil shiver. It made him remember the grief of the royal David weeping for his dead son. "My son, Absolom, Absolom, my son; would to God that I might die for thee, Absolom my son, my son Absolom!"

The grief of David was as nothing compared to that of Jesus. Did Jesus wish he could die for the men whose sins so troubled him?

"Behold," Jesus said, at the end of his lamentation, "your house shall be left to you, desolate!"

Lucifer scurried away. He could no longer bear the look in Jesus' eyes. Wasn't that the way the Most High had looked at him and the other rebellious angels just before he sent them down to hell?

Their house had been left to them desolate indeed!

Lucifer came back when the seventy-two disciples arrived to tell Jesus of their adventures. He jeered as they boasted of the devils they had put to flight. It was true they had evicted some, but Lucifer had found other homes for them — homes in im-portant people too. He thought he had profited in the exchange. He could hardly restrain himself from putting legions of devils into every one of those poor braggarts. But Jesus was watching him, and he was powerless. He always felt like a caged beast in the Messiah's presence.

"I was watching you," Jesus told them. "I saw Satan fall from heaven like lightning. But do not rejoice because evil spirits are subjected to you; rejoice because your names are written in heaven."

In an hour and on a day, which he selected with cunning, Lucifer approached the Apostle Judas, who now carried the purse for Jesus and the others.

"Hail, friend," he said. "Congratulations! The Rabbi has at last discovered your true worth. But he wouldn't have given you this honor if he could have used any of those stupid Galileans. They are his pets, you know. But you have intellect, Friend Judas. You stand out among all these oafs. No wonder you have the purse!"

He knew that Judas was listening to every word.

"Tell me; now that you have cast out devils, cured sick men and women, and worked prodigious miracles — how would you like to be as powerful and famous as your Master? A man who can do the things you have done, and are still doing — why, there's no stopping you! You understand the Rabbi isn't popular with men who count. He is getting less popular every day. The time will come when he will have to flee for his life. What then? What will become of you and these Galilean fools? If you made some sort of deal with the masters of Israel, you might be the Messiah. You yourself! Thus you'd save yourself, and the other disciples. And, perhaps, him too. Think of your life then. You'd not exist on scraps any longer. You'd still have the purse — and you'd find more ways of fattening it than anyone else I know."

It was apparent that Judas liked the words Lucifer put into his mind.

"And those women who do what they can to support you and

the others — Mary Magdalen and the rest — you could get rid of them if you wanted to. Or dispose of them in any way that suited your royal fancy."

It was painful to mention Mary Magdalen's name. She was an arch traitor, and Lucifer hated her beyond all other women, save one. He winced every time he mentioned her name. But then, anything for a soul! He watched Judas and felt encouraged. He had lost the woman. He would gain the man.

"Stay close to your Master for the time being. Study him and everything he does and says. Obey every order. Some day you may be giving orders to him and to those fishermen louts. Keep practicing your miracles; especially in private. And keep looking pious!

"Why not begin now? Aren't you hungry? Remember when your Master put a coin in a fish's mouth for that dunce, Peter? Why don't you better that trick? (And why don't you get rid of Peter? He hates you.) Why don't you change one of those coins into a nice fresh fish? A tasty little pike, say, baked with herbs and butter? Nobody'll miss the coin. And if somebody does, what of it? Didn't your Master say the laborer was worthy of his hire? You heard him with your own ears. Do it then. And what you do, do quickly."

Peter was passing by. Judas called to him. "I am going into town. There is a poor man I know, sadly in need of food."

CHAPTER XX

Lucifer, father of lies, flavored his talk to Judas with enough truth to make the lies believable. It was true that Jesus was unpopular with those in power, and that he was making new and unforgiving enemies every day. It was true that many of the great in Israel were plotting to kill him.

To some of these men in authority it was the most horrible of crimes for a man to call himself the Son of God, or even to hint there was anything in him that was supernatural or superhuman. To them Jesus was the blasphemer of blasphemers. They were honestly opposed to him and everything he did and said. They were offended even by his miracles, for these seemed to proclaim him divine.

Some felt that whether or not he was what he claimed to be, he was still a danger to them. He swayed great crowds wherever he went, whenever he spoke. Such a man was unfair competition. He had a way of healing the sick, no matter what ailed them, thus winning them and their families and friends to his cause. He grew, through comforting and aiding the people. They loved him. Some even adored him! He grew too big too fast. Only one thing would stop him from taking over all Israel!

He could not be handled. He did not negotiate. He did not compromise. He did not take suggestions, nor advice, nor orders.

He issued the orders, made the rules, took command of every situation. He acted on no authority save his own.

He must be killed!

Some believed he might be God as well as man. These resented his interference in the affairs of ordinary men. He could wreck the civilization built and maintained through the centuries by men like themselves. True, that civilization was based on ambition, ruthlessness, avarice, and greed. But it must endure. Jesus, divine or not, was bad for business, bad for government, bad for religion. He might even abolish the Masters of Israel, and give the management of his kingdom to lowborn publicans and sinners! If he were indeed God, then — so be it, so be it — it must be man against God!

Only a few knew him for what he was — almighty God made Man for the love of men; the Creator of men made a Beggar for the love of men; the Author of life come on earth to die for the love of men. Only a few knew what he meant when he said, "Come to me all you that labor and are burdened, and I will refresh you. Take my yoke upon you, and learn of me, because I am meek and humble of heart, and you shall find rest for your souls. For my yoke is sweet and my burden light."

Jesus realized that the more clearly he revealed his divinity, the more desperately his enemies plotted against him. He realized also that, while his being God made some men hate and fear him, it made others — many others — love and adore him. And these would be saved.

Perhaps, at this time, only one sinner truly loved him as Man and as God. This was Mary Magdalen. His Apostles and disciples loved him. They honored and revered him as a holy and powerful prophet, the Messiah sent by God to establish the kingdom of heaven. They loved him for what he appeared to be, and for what he might some day give them. When he came into his own, they would share his glory. The people he had healed, and those he had comforted, and those who had heard him speak, all loved him too, each in his own way. But Mary Magdalen's love — the love of a convert, a penitent — approached the love given him by his sinless virgin mother.

To the Magdalen, Jesus was a divine Man, a human God.

When Jesus met her she was lying ill at the home of her brother Lazarus and her sister Martha in Bethany — just over the Mount of Olives from the city of Jerusalem. She had been a courtesan. She had been rich and famous, and infamous. Everybody who knew her said she was possessed of seven devils. She had run away with a rich Roman officer when she was little more than a child, and had lived for years in the town of Magdala. Now, sick and wretched in heart and spirit because of a lover who had jilted her, she had come back to Bethany.

She looked up through her tears of self-pity, and saw Love Infinite! Tears of remorse washed away the lesser tears. And she saw kindness and compassion, and the forgiveness of her sins. She knew immediately that Jesus was God and Man — her God, her Man.

Jesus loved the house in Bethany where a great sinner was changed into a great saint. He visited it whenever he ventured into Judea. Martha and Lazarus always made a fuss over him. But Mary, if she were present, was content to sit at his feet and drink in every word he uttered, to do nothing but love him! Poor Martha! She was always provoked when Mary wouldn't leave her Lord to help cook, or serve, or do a hundred other things that needed to be done.

When Jesus was present, there was no Martha in the world, no Lazarus. There was no dinner waiting to be prepared. There was nothing but Jesus and his overwhelming love. Martha, who was troubled about many things, did not know that only one was necessary — to give one's whole heart and mind to God and not to worry about anything less than God!

So, though he knew he was multiplying enemies, Jesus continued to reveal himself, especially to the Pharisees and scribes. Some of them must believe in him. Some must be saved.

In a house in Capharnaum he made it quite plain that he was God as well as man. He was teaching there when the miracle occurred. It was an ordinary house. It was made of mud bricks into which much straw had been imbedded. It had two levels. Guests came through the curtains at the open door into a sort of kitchen and farmyard. The cooking was done on this level. The water jars and the kitchen utensils were kept there. And the chickens, a cow and its calf, or an ox, or an ass, might have their quarters there. Two or three steps led to the upper level. A man sat on the steps, had his feet washed, and swung himself around into the living room. This was a hard, leveled, limewashed, clay floor. Here the guests were received, made welcome, served, and entertained.

Jesus sat in the middle of such a floor in this house in Capharnaum, talking of the kingdom of God, which was so different from the world of men — the kingdom of the devil — that the world could scarcely comprehend it. Other men sat all about him, crowding him. The Scribes and Pharisees stood apart, careful that not even the fringes of their garments came into contact with the vulgar horde. When Jesus paused, which he did now and then to let a point sink in, one could hear the clucking of the hens or the clacking of the Pharisees.

There was a great crowd outside the house, some with sick relatives or friends they had brought for Jesus to heal. They waited patiently in the sun. Jesus must come out sometime. But a number were impatient. They had a paralytic with them. They decided not to wait any longer for Jesus to come to them. They would go to Him. They carried their friend on his pallet of straw up the outside stairway to the roof. There they dug away the dirt that covered a carpet of reeds. Then they ripped out a length of the reeds — not a difficult thing to do, since some had rotted long ago — and made a hole between two log rafters, large enough to enable them to lower their friend into the room below. With ropes handled skillfully, they placed the patient on the floor near Jesus.

Jesus watched the men around him scrambling hastily out of the way of the lowered figure of the paralytic. They liked this. This was fun. He watched the Scribes and Pharisees. They were indignant. Jesus welcomed the patient with a smile, and greeted him with words no man had ever said before, no man had ever heard. "Thy sins are forgiven thee."

He noted that His words brought a horrid sort of paralysis to the Pharisees and the Scribes. They were looking up through the hole in the roof as though they expected lightning to flash from the blue and strike the Rabbi for this atrocious blasphemy. Perhaps the bolt would kill them too, for it was a frightful crime to listen to such talk and not immediately take up stones to kill the speaker. Who can forgive sins but the Most High himself? Jesus saw they were raging at their helplessness!

He let them know he read their hearts. He spoke to them as though they were stupid boys "Which is easier to say 'Thy sins are forgiven,' or 'Take up thy bed and go home'?"

They dared not answer lest they trap themselves, lest they make themselves fools before all these ordinary people.

"But that you may know the Son of Man has power on earth to forgive sins," Jesus said, turning away from the holy ones to the patient, "I say to you, take up your bed and go home."

Immediately the man, who until now could not move a muscle, got out of his bed. He stretched himself with wonder and with joy, tears in his eyes. He lifted the bed without effort, and began making his way through the crowded room.

There were explosions of prayer all around him. And there were echoes of it outside the house. The hens caught the contagion and cackled as though they had laid, each one of them, a dozen perfect eggs. The Pharisees, in the confusion, managed to escape — and perhaps without being defiled by the common touch of any of Jesus' followers or friends. They hurried to find some Herodian authorities who would help them put that Blasphemer to death.

On a Sabbath morning, as he and his disciples went through a field of grain, Jesus found another opportunity to proclaim his heavenly power. James and John and Andrew and some of the others had plucked a few ears of grain, for they were hungry. They were rubbing them in their hands — which, under the law as interpreted by the Pharisees and Scribes, might be called "harvesting on the Sabbath" — when their enemies pounced out of ambush, happy to be able to accuse them and their Master.

Jesus took the offensive. "Haven't you read the Scriptures enough to know what David did when he and his men were hungry on a Sabbath?" he demanded, shaming them with their ignorance. "He took his men into the Temple, and they ate the loaves of proposition, which were only for the priests. The Sabbath was made for man, not man for the Sabbath. And the Son of man is Lord of the Sabbath!"

It seemed to the priests that Jesus deliberately sought opportunities to do good on the Sabbath, regardless of their rules. For, on a Sabbath not long after this, he saw a woman stooped over so terribly that she could not look up. She had been in that condition eighteen years. "Woman," he said to her, "thou art delivered from this affliction." He put his hands on her. Immediately she was straight and strong and beautiful. And she glorified God, as did all those witnessing the miracle — all, that is, except the priests.

The ruler of the synagogue, a choleric gentleman, turned purple at this crime. "Six days are given you for work," he shouted to the people standing around. "In those six days, come and be healed. But not on the Sabbath!" If he looked angry, Jesus looked a thousand times angrier, though he did not permit the blood to rush to his face; nor did he shout. "Hypocrites," he said, "There isn't one of you who will not loose his ox or his ass and take him out of the stable for water on the Sabbath. Should this daughter of Abraham, who has been bound for eighteen years, not be loosed from her bond on the Sabbath?"

On another Sabbath, in another synagogue, Jesus saw a man with a withered hand. He had been given one of the first seats, and he was surrounded by Pharisees and Scribes. Hence Jesus knew the man was a trap cunningly baited for him. Jesus never tried to avoid a trap. He never walked around one.

"Stand up," he bade the man. When the man obeyed, Jesus looked at the Scribes and Pharisees, and asked them — politely — if it were lawful to do good on the Sabbath or to do evil, to save life or to destroy it.

They did not answer. They waited for him to act. Then they would wag their tongues.

Jesus, angered by their stupid and cruel plot — more angered than when he loosed the daughter of Abraham from her bond — blasted them with a look. They shrank away from him. The anger of God exceeds the fury of a hundred thousand storms.

"Stretch forth your arm," Jesus said to the man.

The man stretched out his arm, slowly at first, then quickly, easily, joyously. His hand was no longer withered. It was normal.

Jesus had sprung the trap; but no Pharisaic tongue denounced him or even chided him. Yet, when they had left the synagogue and had recovered from their fright, the Pharisees again sought the help of the Herodians — whom they hated — so that they could find a way, all their human wits working together, to end forever the power of this Man who dared perform miracles on the Sabbath.

In Capharnaum Jesus met a delegation of Jews who had an unusual request. They wanted him to cure the servant of a Roman centurion. This man, they said, loved the Jews, and had built a synagogue for them. Also he seemed to love his servant. He would have waited for Jesus, and not sent them as messengers, but he felt unworthy of meeting the great Healer. Jesus went with them willingly. When he drew near the Roman's home, however, the centurion came to meet him, for his servant's condition was bad.

"Lord, I am not worthy that you should enter under my roof," he said, "but only say the word, and my servant shall be healed!"

He was a soldier, he explained, with soldiers under his command. "I say to this one, 'Go,' and he goes; and to another, 'Come,' and he comes; and to my servant, 'Do so and so,' and he does it. Say but the word, Lord, and my servant shall be healed."

Jesus was pleased. He turned to the throngs about him — which included the usual solemn, cynical, suspicious Pharisees and Scribes — and cried out: "Amen I say to you, I have not found such great faith in Israel. And I say to you that many shall come from the east and the west, and shall sit down with Abraham and Isaac and Jacob in the kingdom of heaven. But the children of the kingdom shall be cast out into the exterior darkness, and there shall be weeping and gnashing of teeth."

Some of the masters in Israel gnashed their teeth at hearing this clear warning — accepting it, however not as a warning but as a gesture of defiance, a silly threat. Think of Abraham's children being kicked out of the kindgom while the gentiles poured in from east and west! The Man was mad! Jesus sighed, finding such faith in a Roman, such rejection in his own people!

"Go," he said to the centurion, "and as you have believed, so be it done to you."

Again the masters gnashed their teeth. This man had only to

say a few words, and one he never saw, a common slave, was instantly healed. There must be a simple explanation! Aye, there must be.

But let him raise the dead to life. That was the test of a prophet. Let him try it! He would fail — and he would be discredited. Then all his other miracles would be proved mere tricks.

They followed him and his disciples as they neared the little town of Naim. They saw a funeral procession coming through the gate. On the bier was the body of a young man, the only son of his widowed mother. They saw Jesus comfort the woman and heard him say, "Don't weep." They waited. Jesus was also the only Son of a widowed mother. What would he do?

They saw him approach the bier. Was he going to kneel and ask God to give the dead man back to his mother? Elias had prayed over the child of the widow of Sarepta, stretching himself thrice upon the little body as he prayed. Would Jesus do that? And when he failed — what would he do?

Jesus did not kneel. He voiced no prayer. He simply spoke to the corpse on the stretcher, as though it could hear and obey.

"Young man, I say to thee, 'Arise!' "

One word. A word of command. The soul of the dead man came back to him, like an echo of the word "Arise." And he sat up and began to talk. And there was more life in him than in the Pharisees and Scribes!

It was shortly after this that John the Baptist sent some of his followers to ask Jesus; "Art thou he that is to come; or look we for another?" John was in prison, but Herod had permitted him some small liberties. He was allowed to see his disciples. What he wanted most was news of his Cousin, his Lord and Master.

John knew the answer to the question he had sent his ambassadors to ask; but he wanted his people to know the answer too, so that, when he was dead, they would follow Jesus.

He was still the forerunner of the Messiah, making straight the way.

Jesus entertained John's messengers, and other people, by many miracles, giving them the proofs John had wanted the world to see. "Tell John," he said, "what you have heard and seen. The blind see. The lame walk. Lepers are made clean. The deaf hear. The dead come back to life. The poor have the Gospel preached to them. And blessed is he that is not scandalized in me."

Isaias had prophesied that the Messiah would do all the wonders Jesus had done. He was sending John a message, using Isaias as a code.

It was time, Lucifer decided, to sever all communications between these two. It was time to sever John's head from his body. He listened impatiently, as Jesus lauded John, waiting for an opportunity to coil and strike.

"What went ye out into the desert to see?" Jesus asked. "A reed shaken with the wind? A man clothed in soft garments?" He glanced at the Scribes and Pharisees, and at the Herodians they had brought, like tamed pets, with them. They were dressed in soft garments; and they looked like reeds shaking in the wind — the wind of anger. "But what went you out to see? A prophet? Yea, I say to you, and more than a prophet. This is he of whom it is written: 'Behold I send my angel before thy face, who shall prepare the way before thee.' "

He noticed that the Pharisees understood him. John was the angel sent to prepare the way of the Lord. Hence Jesus must be the Lord. He went on, serenely: "I say to you; among those born of women, there is not a greater prophet than John the Baptist. But he that is the lesser in the kingdom of God is greater than he!"

"I am greater than John the Baptist," Lucifer jeered. "I am greater, for I shall slay him."

Jesus ignored the devil and went on. All the people who heard John, including the publicans, he said, praised God and were baptized with John's baptism. But the Pharisees and the Scribes would have nothing to do with the counsel of God, inviting his wrath against themselves, and were not baptized by him. "And the Lord said, to what shall I liken the men of this generation? They are like children sitting in the market place, saying, 'We have piped to you, and you have not danced. We have lamented and you have not wept.' For John came to you neither eating bread nor drinking wine. And you said he had a devil. The Son of man has come to you eating and drinking; and you say, 'Behold a glutton and a wine sot, a friend of publicans and sinners.' "

As the great multitude began to break up, Lucifer said his say:

"Poor Baptist! He baptized others. He could not baptize himself. Yet worry not, O eloquent Friend of his, I shall baptize him, in my own way, in my own time. I shall baptize him not with water but with wine. You will see me put new wine into that old wineskin, Herod — and wine shall be spilled indeed! The wine of your friend, John. It shall pour out of the chalice of his head, as a libation to my god, Bacchus. I have many gods, as you know, if you are what you say. I make gods more popular than you, gods that attract not mere fishermen and publicans, but the rich and the powerful. And you who know so much about wines and wineskins, tell me — can you put new wine into an old body, once the old wine is spilled? Can you put a live head on a dead body that lacks a head? Can you make head and body one again? Can you use the head of John the Baptist, once it is taken from him? Can you say 'Arise' to the headless body, or the bodiless head?

"You'll miss John. But he goes before you, still, to prepare the way for your going. Your blood too will be spilled like wine. I shall have much pleasure letting it out of the wineskin."

Jesus whisked him away as though he were a buzzing fly.

He knew that John would die, and that many would be scandalized because Jesus had made no effort to save him. Men always tried to measure the unmeasurable ways of God with the inch-long measure of the ordinary man. He showed no emotion when He learned that John was dead.

Herod, said the man who brought the news, had given a party in honor of his birthday. Salome, his wife's daughter, danced for him; and he, being drunk with wine, became so inflamed that he promised her anything she might ask, even to the half of his kingdom. He swore it with an oath. She asked the head of John the Baptist. Herod hesitated, for he was superstitious and dreaded what might happen to a man who killed a prophet. But he would not go back on his oath — for many people had heard him swear it. He sent his swordsman to the dungeon; and John's head was brought back to the banquet hall on a platter.

Jesus walked quietly into the shadows as the messenger talked. He wanted to be alone. He entered a boat, crossed the sea of Galilee, and went into the desert, to speak to his Father, and to his cousin, the last of the great prophets.

CHAPTER XXI

A man who had seen Jesus row across the lake, told his friends; and presently five thousand men, women, and children were walking, through the night, around the shore of the lake-sea. They had listened to Jesus for days; yet they were hungry to hear more. He had wanted to be alone, after hearing of the death of John. They realized that. Or some of them did. But he must not leave them. There was nobody in all the world like him. There never had been. There never would be. He possessed them. They would possess him. They would find him in his desert retreat and keep him with them so long as they might. They had need of him. And, they thought, he had need of them.

For hours and hours they walked, stumbling, falling, fighting sleep, carrying their sick, their maimed, their paralyzed, and their possessed; carrying the baskets that had once contained bread and figs and cheese and olives. At the sight of Jesus they forgot the long march, the weariness, the hunger and thirst, and the fear and anxiety of the night.

Jesus greeted them and immediately began to heal the sick and to cast out devils. After this he talked to them about the kingdom of God, about the love of God, and about the love of neighbor.

Under the spell of his words the day passed swiftly. It was

evening. The people were hungry again and without food. The Apostles spoke to Jesus. "It will soon be dark. Wouldn't it be wise to send these people away now, so they can go into some town and buy food? There is no place in this desert where they can obtain provisions."

"No," Jesus said. "That isn't necessary. You feed them." They were appalled. How were they to feed five thousand wolf-hungry people in the desert?

"We have only five loaves and two fishes," one said, almost in despair. "What is that for so many people?"

"Have them sit down on the grass," Jesus said. "Arrange them in groups of fifty or a hundred."

Lucifer, who had been working on the Apostle Judas, watched, now, every move Jesus made. He sensed the Man was about to perform a miracle. He saw him take a loaf of bread into his hands, look up to heaven as he blessed and broke it, then hand the broken pieces to one of his Apostles. The bread was being multiplied. So was the fish. Out of five loaves of bread, the Man was making thousands. Out of the fish — why he was making fish that never swam in any lake or sea or stream, fish that never even saw a cup of water; and he was making bread that never knew a wheat field, a baking oven, or any woman's hands! Out of five loaves and two fishes he was making food.

"Gather the fragments," Jesus bade the Twelve, when the people had eaten, "lest they be wasted."

The Apostles, each carrying a large basket, went among the people and gathered up what was left. They filled the twelve baskets.

"These leftovers," Lucifer whispered to Judas, "you can sell in the nearest town. There are many poor willing to pay for a handful of that food. One thing you must learn, Judas. Even the poorest of the poor can get money for food if you force him. He will get it even if he has to steal it. Remember that!"

While Jesus was dismissing the crowd, the Apostles, at his orders, got into a boat and started across the water. Jesus went alone to the mountaintop to pray.

A storm blew up when the boat was halfway across the sea. Some of the Apostles remembered the night they were caught in a fearful storm and had awakened Jesus, thinking they were going to die. "Oh ye of little faith!" he had rebuked them. He had said to the wind and the waves, "Peace! Be still!" The sea had immediately calmed. The wind became a zephyr. They were not afraid now. They belonged to Jesus, and he would protect them. But even as they congratulated themselves on their courage and their faith, they saw something coming toward them across the waters that chilled them with unholy dread.

There had been a bright moon when they set out to cross the sea; now it was obscured by thin layers of clouds. Whatever the menace might be, it could not be readily identified. It might be a monster out of the depths. It might be a land beast swimming. It looked like a man walking on the water, so perhaps it was a ghost. Their teeth were chattering with fright, but they managed to call on God for help.

It was a Man. He was walking on the troubled water as though it were a soft carpet on a hard, level floor. They didn't believe it until the Man came close enough for them to see he was Jesus. "Be of good heart," he said. "It is I. Have no fear."

Peter, still doubting what he saw and heard, answered like a man waking out of a nightmare: "Lord, if it be thou, bid me come to thee."

"Come," Jesus said. Peter leaped out of the boat and walked a few steps. Lucifer halted him, saying, "Don't be a fool; look at the waves all around you; and listen to that wind! Do you want to drown?" Peter listened and began to sink. "Lord save me," he shouted. Jesus took him by the hand, as a father might take a child, and led him to the ship. "O thou of little faith," he said, "why did you doubt me?"

Lucifer decided he would try Peter again.

The wind ceased when Jesus helped Peter into the boat. Then all the Apostles knelt at their Master's feet, and adored him. "Thou art indeed the Son of God!" each one said.

Lucifer began to doubt again. The Man called himself Lord of the Sabbath. The winds and waves obeyed him. The water was like the solid earth to him. He multiplied loaves and fishes. He cured all sorts of people. He even raised the dead. He might indeed be the Son of God! Lucifer wavered. No. That was impossible. He was Joseph's son. The Pharisees were right. He was a mere blasphemer!

The boat was moored at Genesareth. The people recognized Jesus as soon as he went ashore. Hence new crowds came with their sick and crippled; some venturing merely to touch his garments to be cured. While he was ministering to these, most of the people he had fed the previous evening joined them, some pushing their way close enough to ask, "Rabbi, when did you get here?"

Jesus was not pleased to see them, for he knew the motive that had made them pursue him.

Sometime before this, after his seventy-two disciples had reported what they discovered in the areas they had visited, Jesus had publicly thanked his Father for the love and the faith shown by these "little ones."

"I confess to thee, O Father, Lord of heaven and earth," he had cried — to the scandal of the Pharisees — "because thou hast hidden these things from the wise and prudent and revealed them to the little ones."

Jesus, who lived in eternity as well as time, saw countless generations of "little ones" going to heaven through love and faith.

"All things are delivered to me by my Father," he had declared. "No one knows the Son but the Father. Neither does anyone know the Father except the Son, and he to whom it shall please the Son to reveal him."

Through those disciples Jesus had revealed the Father to the humble people of Galilee. Last night he had revealed the Father to those he had fed so bounteously with so little.

It was the Father who had made the earth, and put wheat in it — wheat he multiplied so it would feed the world. It was the Father who had made all the waters, and stocked them with fish, who had made the grass on which they sat, the homing birds that flew above them as they ate, the moon and the stars that gave them light, the cool wind that refreshed them, and — indeed — themselves and all those about them.

And he had sent to them his only-begotten Son, that they might learn about love, the food of the soul!

But the people hadn't seen God at all. They saw only a Man who might do great things for them, who might set up the new Israel of their dreams, who might lead them to conquest and slaughter, make them masters of creation, and give them such abundance and comfort as never was known before. This generation was not of the spirit. It was distinctly of the flesh.

He scolded them mildly, because they were willing to work hard and to fight hard for the sort of bread that could not last, and because they did nothing to obtain the bread that "would endure to life everlasting."

He had that Bread, he told them. And he would gladly give it to all who asked for it.

Instead of asking immediately for this Bread, they asked for a sign. Other crowds had also demanded a sign of Jesus — at the prompting of the Pharisees — and Jesus had answered: "An evil and adulterous generation seeks a sign; and no sign shall be given it except the sign of Jonas the prophet. For as Jonas was in the whale's belly three days and three nights, so shall the Son of man be in the heart of the earth three days and three nights. The men of Ninive shall rise in judgment with this generation, and shall condemn it; because they did penance at the preaching of Jonas. And, behold, a greater than Jonas is here! The queen of the south shall rise in judgment with this generation, and shall condemn it. Because she came from the ends of the earth to hear the wisdom of Solomon, and behold a greater than Solomon is here!"

But with this crowd, Jesus was patient. "What sign do you give us?" they asked. "Our fathers ate manna in the desert. It is written! 'He gave them bread from heaven to eat.' Can you do as much?"

"Amen, amen, I say to you, Moses did not give you bread from heaven," Jesus said. "But my Father does. He gives you the true Bread from heaven. The Bread of God is that which comes down from heaven and gives life to the world."

After a moment of deep silence, a few shouted: "Lord, give us this bread always." Jesus looked at them with a great pity. They did not understand. They would not understand. But he must say what he had to say, whether they understood or not.

"I am the Bread of life," he told them. "Who comes to me shall not hunger. Who believes in me shall never thirst."

Lucifer whispered, first to the stunned Judas, then to others in the crowd. "First he is the Son of a carpenter in Nazareth. Now he is bread from heaven, and he is going to feed the world!" Men began to repeat his words. They began to cough and spit. A few laughed as though they had heard a silly joke but didn't quite appreciate it.

Jesus asked for silence, then went on: "I am the Bread of life. Your fathers ate manna in the desert, but they died. I am the living Bread that came down from heaven. If any man eat of this Bread, he shall live forever!"

He was talking not like a man now. He was speaking as God. And they hissed at him like a lot of silly geese.

"Eat and live forever? Came down from heaven? Living Bread? Bread of life?" They shook the words out of their minds like geese shaking dust out of their feathers.

Jesus regarded them with infinite sorrow. He had said to them, a short time ago: "It is the will of my Father, who sent me, that everyone who sees the Son, and believes in him, may have life everlasting. And I will raise him up on the last day." And, a short time ago, he had also said: "No man can come to me unless my Father draw him. . . . Everyone who has heard of the Father, and has learned of God, comes to me. . . . Amen, amen, I say unto you, he who believes in me has everlasting life."

They had seen him; and they did not believe in him. They had come to him; but it was not his Father who drew them toward him. Nor was it the urging of their hearts. Their stomachs had sent them; their hunger not for love and peace and happiness, but for comfort, luxury, influence, power, wealth.

"And the Bread that I will give," he said, "is my flesh — for the life of the world!"

Those close to him recoiled as though he had spit upon them. How could anyone give his flesh to others as food? Would he kill himself first? Then how would he divide himself among those eager to gnaw his bones? Would he multiply himself as he had done with the loaves and fishes? The Man was mad! And did he think they were dogs slavering for the unclean food of human flesh? Or barbaric cannibals?

Jesus did not try to explain, nor to soften his message, nor to appease those suddenly hostile to him. Rather he confirmed what he had said, using even clearer and more terrible language:

"Amen, amen, I say unto you, except you eat the flesh of the Son of man, and drink his blood, you shall not have life in you!"

"Blood!" Lucifer sent the word hurtling through the minds of the crowd. "He wants you to drink his blood, like wild beasts. Moses has said, 'Beware thou eat not the blood of an animal, for the blood is for the soul; thou must not eat the soul with the flesh.' This Man wants you not only to swallow down his flesh, but his blood as well. Is he greater, then, than Moses?"

The crowd murmured again. But Jesus was still in full command. And he had more to say. "He that eats my flesh and drinks my blood has everlasting life. And I will raise him up in the last day. For my flesh is meat indeed. And my blood is drink indeed. He that eats my flesh and drinks my blood abides in me, and I in him. As the living Father has sent me, and I live by the Father, so he that eats me shall live by me."

He could not help mourning for these poor ignorant and stubborn children. He had told them he was God, since only God could raise up a soul on the last day. He was God, and he was offering them his body and soul, his humanity and divinity. But they would have none of him, nor anything he offered!

The all-seeing, all-knowing Son of Man had been rejected by the stupid and the blind! Even worse, he had become to them a creature more repulsive than a leper!

Mothers whose babies he had held and blessed only a little while ago, fathers who had rejoiced with him when he cured their children that morning, the blind and the deaf and the lame and the arthritic who had shown such hope and faith when they touched his garments — and who had been instantly healed — were backing away from him as though he were accursed!

Yet he had known they would reject him. He could expect other rejections. He was used to rejection. Joseph had rejected him when he lay in the womb of Mary. It required the visit of an angel to make Joseph accept him. Innkeeper after innkeeper had sent him away. A king had tried to murder him when he was but a few months old. He had been rejected by boys of his own age, because he was so different from them. He had been rejected as an adolescent and as a mature man. His priests had rejected him when he went to the Temple to teach and preach. He had been rejected by his old neighbors in Nazareth. They had wanted to kill him. Many others had wanted to kill him. Now the crowds who had followed him for so many days, who had looked up to him, and who had depended on him, had deliberately abandoned him. Some of his disciples had gone with them; and they would not return.

And he knew that only the shedding of his blood, "his soul," would bring any of them back. He turned to his Apostles. "Are you also scandalized in me?" he asked. "Will you also leave me?" Peter spoke out, belligerently glaring at the others. "Lord, to whom shall we go? You have the words of eternal life. We have believed in you. We know you are the Christ, the Son of God."

Jesus nodded. Peter would reject him too. So would all the others, save only John. They would return to him though, and they would give their lives in atonement. One would not only reject him; he would also sell Him.

"One of you," Jesus said, "is a devil."

Lucifer, afraid Judas would speak, bade him hold his tongue.

"Just look dumb," he suggested. "And pious. And stay with him until your hour comes. . . ."

Lucifer was too shaken to say more. The words of Jesus had thrown him into as great a panic as his baptism by John had done. He sensed that something new and frightful was threatening hell's hold on mankind. It was the more frightening because it was so vague. Jesus had not explained what he meant about offering his flesh and blood to the people. Surely there was a spiritual explanation he could have offered. Why hadn't he offered it? Was it because the people had no feeling for things spiritual? Was it because an explanation would increase their confusion and harden their opposition to him? Was it because Jesus didn't think the time was right for any explanation?

Perhaps Jesus didn't care whether the people understood him or not, so long as they heeded what he said. Evidently he wanted a blind obedience from them, a childlike trust. Evidently he placed faith above intelligence. He was a Man who seldom explained his words or his actions except, for all Lucifer knew to the contrary, to his disciples in privacy. He was a Man no other man could ever completely understand. But it was not understanding he wanted. He wanted love.

And then, too, maybe he wanted to keep Lucifer as long as possible, in the torment of helpless ignorance.

CHAPTER XXII

Jesus, as God, was not surprised at his rejection by the people he so loved and pitied. He had always known exactly what would happen. Nor was he discouraged, for he saw the future. But as a man, he was hurt, dispirited, and depressed. Galilee had become not only suspicious of him since he offered his flesh and blood as meat and drink, but even hostile. The crowds, that had given him no rest, now avoided him as though he carried all the plagues that ever cursed the earth. And they kept the children from him.

As a man, he needed solace, understanding, encouragement, and love. No man had ever begged so hard for the love of men. No man had ever valued love so highly. No man had ever done so much to earn love. No man had ever been so wantonly denied the love that was due him.

His Apostles loved him, of course, each in his own way; but none had any real understanding of him, nor any appreciation of his needs. They could not give him the least encouragement in this dark hour. They felt discouraged too. And they were afraid, for the political situation had changed with the death of John. Herod, hearing of the miracles performed in his kingdom by Jesus of Nazareth, was sure that John had risen from the dead. And at any time he might summon Jesus to appear at his court. Or he might send soldiers to arrest him.

Where could Jesus go? And where could they go, if they followed him? Judea was no longer safe. Every day there were more plots against him, more traps built for him. He could go only to the north, to the regions governed by Herod's brother, Philip. He would be free of Herod there. He would be free of the schemers in Judea. He would be free of the embittered people of Capharnaum, and of Galilee in general.

Jesus decided to take his Apostles into the villages of Caesarea Philippi. He would return to Judea later, when it was the appointed time. But first he must visit his mother.

In her he would find the sympathy and encouragement he needed. He would find inspiration too, and all the joy any human creature could extend him. (Millions and millions of Mary's other children would follow him — in moments of sorrow, or pain, or agony of soul, or fear, or desperate need. And never would it be known that any of them was left unaided.)

As Jesus turned in the direction of her little house, scores of birds began to fly around him, singing hymns of praise and thanks. His mother's lovely friends. Birds came to Mary every day, sometimes only a few, sometimes great flocks of them. Jesus remembered a morning when he saw his mother walking toward him and Joseph through a field of wild flowers. The air around her was filled with flashing red and blue and gold and snow-white wings. Feathered wings. Lacy wings. Painted paper wings of butterflies and moths. Gossamer wings of dragonflies. Burnished wings of bettles. Jeweled wings of hummingbirds and honeybees. And the glowing lights of fireflies, that, even in the daylight, made a winking unsteady halo around her queenly head.

The flowers through which she came also had wings that folded and unfolded, keeping pace with her! All the beauties of nature seemed, that morning, to be paying tribute to the Queen of Beauty.

Jesus had called the attention of his foster father to the

spectacle, but the only beauty Joseph saw was the beauty of his wife. He noticed neither butterflies nor birds nor insects. He most likely did not even see the flowers that blessed her little feet.

The birds shot up toward the low-lying clouds as Jesus approached the house, and the Apostles watched in wonder. The mud bricks of the house had been newly limed. They looked and smelled fresh and inviting. There were flowers all around the house. And there would be more, Jesus knew, inside the house. Wherever Mary was, flowers bloomed and flourished.

She was alone when Jesus came through the door, which was unusual, for she gave herself to many people. In the mornings the children of the neighborhood used to come to have her look at their eyes, their teeth, their ears, their hair. Mary had a wonderful way of making the little ones shine, as their mothers had discovered. She was better than a doctor and a nurse combined. Besides, she told the children stories, and gave them good things to eat and drink.

Women came later in the day to ask for help, advice, consolation, sympathy, recipes, or news. Someone always brought news to Mary.

Several times, when Jesus was preaching in the fields near Capharnaum, Mary had gone out with her nephews and nieces, to fill herself with the joy of looking at him and listening to his words. On one of these occasions Jesus, learning his relatives were in the crowd, turned to those close to him, and with a meaning gesture said; "Behold my mother and my brethren! Whoever does the will of God is my brother, my sister, my mother."

Salome had been disturbed by those words. "He is not ashamed of us," Mary explained. "He is merely trying to make the people identify themselves with him. All those men and women really are his close relatives. They are even closer to him than blood kinship when they do the will of God. So let us always be sure we do God's will, not our own."

She had been enraptured with him and with the things he said; but she could not neglect those who came to her each day, and who relied on her for what they so badly needed. She felt it was the will of God that she stay at home and minister to the poor. She kept in touch with her Son only through the news friends brought her.

"He cured ten lepers, but only one returned to thank him. Do you suppose the priests told the others to stay away from him?" . . . "He drove a legion of devils out of a naked wild man everybody feared. They went into a drove of swine. The swine rushed into the water and drowned. Thousands of them, I heard. The people came running up when they saw the hogs dive into the water. And they asked Jesus to go away. They would rather have their pigs than Jesus!" . . . "And then a Cañaanite woman asked him to rid her daughter of a devil. At first he wouldn't talk to her. But she persisted. Then he said he had come only to the children of Israel, and it wasn't fair to take the bread of those children and throw it to the dogs. Wouldn't you think the woman would take that as a slap in the face? Wouldn't you think she'd go on about her business? Not this one! She said that even the dogs ate the crumbs that fell from their masters' table. Imagine that! Jesus knew, of course, that she would say exactly that. He wanted everybody to see what humility she had, and what great faith. 'O woman,' he said, 'great is your faith. Be it done as you will.' At first I thought he was being rude, and I was shocked. It was so unlike him. But afterwards I began to see what he was about. . . ."

"There was a little girl, the daughter of Jairus, the ruler of a synagogue. Jesus went to her house because her father asked him to. He brought three of his Apostles with him. Peter, James, and

John. The girl was dead, and everybody was carrying on when Jesus arrived. They laughed when he said the girl was not dead. I guess they had forgotten about the widow's son in Naim — or maybe they hadn't heard how he raised him from the bier. Anyway the fools laughed. Jesus went to the child, took her hand, and said to her 'Arise.' The very word he said to the dead man in Naim. She rose up. She was alive again. She ran to her mother. And Jesus had to remind everybody that the girl was hungry and needed food. . . ."

"Your Son has a tremendous love for children. I just heard how he put a child in the midst of his Apostles. They had been quarreling about who was to be the greatest in the kingdom of heaven. He made them understand that, unless they became as little children, they would not enter the kingdom. Whoever humbled himself as a little child, he said, would be the greatest in the kingdom. And, he said, whoever caused one of the little ones who believed in him to commit a sin, it were better he had a millstone tied to his neck and he were cast into the sea. 'Let the little children come unto me,' he said, 'for of such is the kingdom of heaven. Whoever receives a child for my sake, receives me. And who receives me receives him who sent me. . . .' "

"He cursed a fig tree because it could bear fruit but didn't. I know several couples who could bear children, but will not. How does he feel about such people, I wonder." . . . "He is against divorce. 'What God has joined together,' he said, 'let no man put asunder.' He says that whoever puts away his wife and marries another commits adultery against her; and the wife commits adultery if she puts away her husband and marries some other man."

"Yesterday Jesus said, 'Where two or three are gathered in my name, there am I in the midst of them.' So he is here with us. Now."

"Jesus was talking about a rich farmer. He had such an

abundance of food he didn't know what to do with it all. He decided to build bigger barns. That would give him more storage space. That meant he must acquire more acres. He rejoiced in his riches and told his soul not to worry. He would eat, drink, and be merry. Then, suddenly, one night God said to him, 'You fool, this moment is your soul demanded of you.' . . ."

Only once did Mary make any comment on the news she heard. That was when some woman spoke of Jesus and his praise of John the Baptist. "He said John was the greatest man born of woman. Was John then greater than Joseph, your Son's father?"

"Some say Jesus declared John was the greatest man," Mary answered, "and others that he was the greatest phophet. But Jesus added that one who was not so high in the kingdom of God was even greater than John. Joseph belonged to the kingdom. He was a man of great simplicity and self-abasement; yet he made a man of the Son of Heaven. He was a man hidden in God. And God was hidden in him. He was the tutor of the Messiah. He was the prince regent of the kingdom for nearly thirty years. Jesus obeyed him implicitly. And Jesus loved and honored him above all other men."

Not everything Jesus did or said was reported to Mary. But she was content. Once she had not been able to let him out of her sight. Now she was resigned to his leaving her for weeks and months. To do his will, and only his will, was all that mattered.

Mary was sitting on a mat near the door when Jesus came to visit her. She was patching an old mantel. A shadow came between her and the light. She looked up and saw the Light of the world! She had not expected to see him, though she knew he was in Capharnaum.

He was her Son. She never could forget that. Yet he was her God too. She could not forget that either. And one who looks at God, even for the ten thousandth time, is the special guest of heaven.

They did not say more than a few words to each other. They had little need of words. Heaven looked at heaven, gloried in the power and the wisdom and the riches of almighty God, and mourned the weakness and the stupidity and the poverty of God's poor children.

Birds came singing into the house. Jesus blessed his mother, and turned to go. He gathered his Apostles about him, and started down the road to the north, strong, confident, serene. His mother stood in the doorway a long time, unmindful of the singing birds, looking after him and his followers and the dust they raised. She prayed that she might see him as least once more before he died . . . if it was God's will.

Great consolations awaited Jesus in the North. Thinking of Herod and the king's belief that John the Baptist had come to life in the person of Jesus, he asked his Apostles; "Who do men say I am?" They answered. "Some say you are John the Baptist. Others think you are Elias, or Jeremias, or one of the other prophets."

"And you," Jesus asked, "who do you say I am?"

Peter answered: "You are Christ, the Son of the living God."

Jesus rejoiced at this. "Blessed are you, Simon Bar-Jona," he said. "Flesh and blood has not revealed this to you, but my Father in heaven. And I say to you, you are Peter [a rock], and on this rock I will build my Church; and the gates of hell shall not prevail against it. And I will give you the keys of the kingdom of heaven. Whatever you bind on earth shall be bound in heaven. Whatever you loose on earth shall be loosed in heaven. But, mind you, tell no one I am the Christ."

And within a week after this he heard his father's voice.

He had taken Peter and James and John up a high mountain that they might pray by themselves. The Apostles, tired with their exertion, fell asleep on their knees, but woke, suddenly, to the awareness that something beautiful and strange had happened to the Master!

His face shone more brightly than the sun. His clothing radiated light. And, as the astonished trio looked on, not quite sure they were awake, two men appeared with him, clothed in glory also. The Apostles identified one as Moses and the other as Elias. They listened for a moment or two, but without much attention, for the prophets were speaking of the death Jesus was to die in Jerusalem; and that subject seemed both untimely and untactful to Peter and James and John.

Peter had to say something, anything, for he could not stand this talk of death. It frightened him. It frightened the others too.

"Lord," Peter said, "it is good to be here. Let us set up three tents. One for you. One for Moses. And one for Elias."

He stopped, suddenly, for a bright cloud enshrouded him and the "sons of thunder"; and he heard an awesome voice speaking out of it. "This is my beloved Son in whom I am well pleased; hear him."

Jesus could not help rejoicing at such words from the throne of heaven. No other man could know the happiness they gave him.

The Apostles shielded their faces from the intolerable light and prostrated themselves in abject fear until Jesus bade them rise and take heart. When they uncovered their eyes they saw he was alone, his usual Self. He bade them tell no man what they had seen — until the Son of man had "risen from the dead."

Many times, now, Jesus talked to his followers about the death that waited him in the holy city. He would be tortured and put to death by the elders and the Scribes and the chief priests, he told them. But on the third day he would rise from the tomb.

Peter, on one occasion — one occasion only — ventured to chide the Lord for such talk. The Lord rebuked him severely.

"Get behind me, Satan," he said. "You are a scandal to me, for you do not pay attention to the things of God, but those of men!"

Then he gave the Apostles a hint of the death planned for him. "If any man will come after me, let him deny himself, and take up his cross, and follow me. For he that will save his life shall lose it; and he that shall lose his life for my sake, shall find it. For what doth it profit a man if he gain the whole world, and suffer the loss of his soul? Or what shall a man give in exchange for his soul?"

Yet he must give them some comfort, even as he needed comfort.

"The Son of man," he promised, "shall come in the glory of his father with his angels; and then will he render to every man according to his works. Amen I say to you, there are some of them that stand here, that shall not taste death until they see the Son of man coming in his kingdom."

CHAPTER XXIII

At the right time, the moment selected by His Father, Jesus started to Judea with His Apostles, knowing that his enemies swarmed through that section of the world, hopeful to ensnare and slay him.

As he passed through Galilee, Zebedee's wife came to beg him to honor her sons, John and James, to place them, one at his right side and one at his left, when he came into his kingdom. Jesus had told his followers again and again that he was going to Jerusalem to be mocked and scourged and crucified, but they had paid little or no attention to him. They still believed he was establishing a temporal kingdom, and each wanted to share his glory. Now he turned to James and John and asked if they could drink the chalice he would drain. They nodded. They could, they said.

"You shall indeed drink my chalice," he said. "But it is not for me to say where you shall sit. My Father will seat whom he wishes near me. But whoever shall be the greatest among you, let him serve the others; even as the Son of man has come to serve, not to be served, and to give his life for the redemption of many."

They had been resting in the shade of the wind-twisted and bent olive and fig trees on the shore of the Sea of Galilee, enjoying the iodine smell of the sea, the dark blue of the water and the light blue of the sky, the sound made by the little waves breaking on the stones, the feel of the sand and earth beneath them, the odor of the growing things about them. And Jesus taught them the prayer that makes all the people of the world one family, the children of God, brothers and sisters of one another.

"Our Father, who art in heaven, hallowed be thy name. Thy kingdom come, thy will be done, on earth as it is in heaven. Give us this day our daily bread, and forgive us our trespasses as we forgive those who trespass against us. And lead us not into temptation. But deliver us from evil. Amen."

Prayer, he told them, beat against the door of heaven until God rose to answer. "Ask," he assured them, "and it shall be given you. Seek and you will find. Knock and it shall be opened to you. If you ask your father for bread, will he give you a stone? If you ask for fish, will he give you a serpent? Well, if you, being evil, know how to give good gifts to your children, how much more readily will your Father in heaven give the Holy Spirit to those who ask him?"

It was on the way to Judea that Jesus disclosed the standards of heaven. He spoke of the King of heaven as using these standards in judging souls. They would be judged according to the way they treated others.

"Come, ye blessed of my Father. Possess the kingdom prepared for you from the foundation of the world. For I was hungry and you gave me to eat; thirsty and you gave me drink. I was a stranger and you took me in; naked and you covered me; sick and you visited me; in prison and you came to see me. . . .

"Depart from me, ye cursed, into everlasting fire, which was prepared for the devil and his angels. For I was hungry and you gave me nothing to eat; thirsty and you gave me no drink. I was a stranger and you did not ask me in; naked and you did not clothe me; sick and in prison and you neglected me . . ."

And when the souls would ask when had they seen him

hungry or thirsty, sick, naked, a prisoner or a stranger, the Lord God, their Judge, Jesus said, would answer: "So long as you did it to one of these my least brethren, you did it to me."

Or he would say: "So long as you did not do it to one of these, you did not do it to me."

In Jerusalem, Jesus taught daily in the Temple; and daily his foes did their best to discredit him, make him look ridiculous, or cause him to do something or say something that might lead to his destruction. In one attempt they used a woman.

"Master," they said, "this one was taken in adultery. Moses, in the law, commanded that such a sinner should be stoned. What do You say?"

They stood around Jesus, apparently in the deepest respect. The people must not suspect they were plotting against the Messiah. The woman they placed before him. She was young, and so shamed she could not look at the great Prophet to whom they had brought her.

The Scribes and Pharisees had no regard for her feelings. They were going to stone her anyway, whatever Jesus said. But he must say something. He must say that Moses was wrong — and therefore turn the people against him. Or he must say Moses was right, and give orders for the stones to fly. Then they would remind him that he had said, many times, he had come to save sinners, not to judge them. He had once said he was the good shepherd. He knew his sheep and his sheep knew him. He would leave the ninety and nine in the fold and go everywhere seeking the sheep that was lost. And when he found it, he would carry it tenderly home on his shoulder. He had said that a shepherd would die for his flock. What about this lost sheep? Would he die for her? Or would he order her slaughtered?

Jesus bowed low, so that the woman might not be further embarrassed, and wrote with his finger on the ground.

"Let him that is without sin," he said, "cast the first stone."

This was an answer they did not expect. It startled them. More, it frightened them. That moving finger was writing not only on the ground, it was writing on their minds, their consciences, their hearts. It was the finger of God writing their sins in scarlet and black. They went away, the eldest first, as quickly as they might.

When all the accusers had gone, Jesus spoke to the woman.

"Has no man condemned you?"

"No man, Lord."

Jesus dismissed her gently. "Neither do I condemn thee. Go and sin no more."

The woman walked away in freedom, joyful and wondering. Through an ugly sin she had been brought close to the Lord. Through the forgiveness of that sin, she had known his love!

Jesus turned to the people who remained. "I am the Light of the world," he told them. "He who follows me does not walk in the dark, but shall have the light of life. . . . If you continue in my word you shall be my disciples indeed. And you shall know the truth, and the truth will make you free."

There were some who were puzzled about that remark. They were the children of Abraham, they reminded him; and had never been slaves to any man. How, then, could he make them free? He told them they were the slaves of sin; but that the Son of God could make them free.

"I know you are the children of Abraham," he said; "but you seek to kill me, because my word has no place in your hearts. I preach that which I have seen with my Father; and you do the things you have seen your fathers do."

"Abraham is our father," one said. The crowd was still hostile.

"Then do the works of Abraham," Jesus answered. "But now you want to kill me, a Man who has spoken to you truths which I heard from God. Abraham did not act thus."

"We have one Father," another said. "God!"

Jesus was not impressed. "If God were your Father," he said, "you would love me; for he sent me here. Why do you not listen to me? You cannot bring yourselves to hear me. You are the children of the devil, and you obey the wishes of your father. He was a murderer from the beginning. And a liar. And the father of lies. Which of you can convict me of sin? I tell you the truth. Why do you not believe me? He that is of God hears the words of God. You do not listen to them because you are not of God."

Now others lifted up their voices. "Do not we say well that you are a Samaritan, and that you have a devil?"

Jesus said simply. "I have not a devil. I honor my Father. You have dishonored me. But I do not seek my own glory. There is One who seeks — and judges. Amen, amen, I say to you; if any man keep my word, he shall not see death forever."

"Now we know you have a devil," some of His enemies shouted. "Abraham and the prophets are all dead. But you say 'if any man keep my word, he shall not taste death forever.' Are you greater than our father, Abraham, who is dead? Are you greater than the dead prophets? Whom do you make yourself?"

Jesus said calmly, "If I glorify myself, my glory is nothing. It is my Father who glorifies me — my Father whom you call your God. You have not known him. But I know him. If I were to say I did not know him, I would be a liar, like yourselves. I know him, and I keep his word. Abraham, your father, rejoiced that he might see my day. He saw it and was glad."

The hecklers were stunned for a moment, then angry enough to murder Him. "You are not fifty years old," they said, "and you have seen Abraham?"

Jesus stunned them again with his calm answer.

"Amen, Amen, I say to you, before Abraham was, I am!" He was calling himself God! God Who Is! They picked up

stones to kill him. But he disappeared. One moment they had
made a ring around him. One moment they were looking murder
at him out of their flaming eyes. The next moment they were
looking murder only at each other.

The next to bring Jesus into conflict with those who hated him
was a man who had been blind from the moment he was born.
This man sat on the Temple steps all day and begged of those
who came to worship. He was known to all Jerusalem. The
Apostles called attention to him by asking who had sinned that
he should be punished with blindness, himself or his parents?
They thought blindness was a punishment sent directly from
heaven.

Jesus corrected that idea. This man, he said, was an instru-
ment chosen by God to show his wonders.

"I must do the works of him who sent me," he said. "I am
the Light of the world, so long as I am in the world. The night
comes, however, when no man can work. I must work while it
is day." When he had said this, he spat on the ground, made
a little mud out of the earth, and spread it over the beggar's
eyes.

Did God the Father thus use the slime of the earth to make
the first man? Did he thus model his eyes?

"Now go wash in the pool of Siloe," Jesus said. The beggar
did so, and received his sight. And many people wondered.
Some recognized him. Others did not. A few knew he was the
beggar who had sat right there on the steps for years, day after
day, a man born blind. How, then, could he now see? "A man
named Jesus cured me," the beggar told everybody. "He told
me what to do. I did it. And I see."

Friends brought the man to the Pharisees; and the Pharisees
questioned him. He told them exactly what he had told the
others. The Pharisees didn't like that. And they were especially
angry because the man had been cured on the Sabbath.

"This man, Jesus," one said, "is not of God, since he does not keep the Sabbath."

Others said, "But how can anyone do such a miracle if he be not of God?"

They turned again on the beggar. What did he think of Jesus? "He is a prophet," the man declared. That made some of the Pharisees wonder if the man had really been blind. Maybe he was a fraud. They sent for his parents and questioned them; but the parents were wary of the Pharisees, and careful of saying too much. They did not want to be put out of the synagogue.

"This is our son," they admitted. "And he was indeed born blind. Who opened his eyes? We don't know. Ask him. He is of age. He can speak for himself." Again the Pharisees summoned the blind man who now could see. They asked him to denounce Jesus as a sinner and give the glory solely to God. "Whether or not he be a sinner I don't know," the man told them. "One thing I do know. Whereas I was born blind, now I see."

"What did he do to you?" they demanded, starting the inquisition all over again. "How did he open your eyes?"

"I have told you already," the man said, stoutly. (No wonder God loves men!) "You heard me. Why do you want to hear it again? Will you become his disciples?"

They reviled him for those words, and they reviled Jesus, which made the former blind man rise to heroic heights.

"This is odd!" he said. "You do not know whether he is from God or the devil. Yet he has opened my eyes. From the beginning of the world, never has it been heard that anyone has opened the eyes of one born blind. Unless this Man were of God he could do nothing."

The Pharisees could say only, "You were born in sin, and you would teach us?" Then they cast him out of the Temple.

Jesus asked him: "Do you believe in the Son of God?"

"Who is he, Lord? Tell me, that I may believe in him."

"You are looking at him," Jesus said. "He is speaking to you."

"I believe, Lord," the man said. And, falling down at Jesus' feet, he adored him.

"I have come into this world for judgment," Jesus said, "that they who see not, may see; and they who see, may become blind."

A Pharisee who overheard this asked him: "Are we also blind?"

"If you were blind," Jesus said, "you would not have sin. But you say that you see. Your sin remains."

Jesus spoke also to the Pharisees of his coming death and resurrection.

"I lay down my life for my sheep," he told them. "Other sheep I have that are not of this fold. Them also I must bring. They will hear my voice, and there shall be one fold and one Shepherd. Therefore does the Father love me; because I lay down my life that I may take it up again. No man takes it away from me. I lay it down of myself; and I have power to lay it down. And I have power to take it up again. . . .

"You do not believe, because you are not my sheep. My sheep know my voice and follow me. I give them life everlasting. They shall not perish forever, and no man shall pluck them out of my hand. That which my Father has given me is greater than all; and no one can snatch it out of the hand of my Father. I and the Father are one."

Again the Pharisees took up stones.

"Many good works have I showed you, through the power given me by my Father," Jesus said. "For which one of these works do you stone me?"

"We stone you not for any good work," they said, "but for blasphemy; because you, an ordinary man, make yourself God!"

Once more murder menaced Jesus — but when the stones were lifted, he had again mysteriously disappeared.

CHAPTER XXIV

For the sake of his Apostles, who were frightened at his continual danger, and because it was not yet the hour for him to suffer, Jesus left Jerusalem, and went beyond the Jordan where John had baptized him. There he remained for some time, preaching to many people, healing the sick, teaching the love of God and the love of neighbor. Messengers sent by Martha and Mary, the sisters of Lazarus, found him there, and told him Lazarus was ill.

"He will survive," Jesus said. "This sickness is for the glory of God, that the Son of God may be glorified by it."

But two days later he gathered his Apostles about him, and suggested they return to Judea. They thought this was madness. The Pharisees were still hoping to bury him under a pile of stones. And he would go back to them?

"Are there not twelve hours in a day?" he asked them. "If a man walk in the day he does not stumble, because he sees the light of this world. But he stumbles if he walk in the night, because the light is not in him." They had no idea what he meant, but there was some comfort in the way he said it. They recalled that He once had said, "I am the Light of the world." Perhaps he meant that he would be safe in Judea. Perhaps he meant something else.

Then he puzzled them with another statement; "Our friend Lazarus sleeps. I go to wake him." They said that if Lazarus slept he was all right, he would get well. Then Jesus told them plainly, Lazarus was dead.

"And I am glad, for your sakes," he added, "that I was not in Bethany, so that you may believe. Let us go to him."

Thomas knew only one thing for certain. Jesus was going to Bethany, which was near Jerusalem. And he was going to his death. Thomas sighed, and looked around about him, at the swirling green water, the luxuriant trees and grasses, the wealth of wild flowers, the flocks of birds, the pleasant sky — as though he might never see any of these things again.

"Come on," he said to the others. "Let's go, that we may die with him." They nodded. They too were willing to die with Jesus, it seemed. At least they did not hold back. They followed the Master as they had since first he called them.

On the outskirts of Bethany, Martha came to meet them. She had heard that Jesus was coming and had left the house at once. Mary had stayed behind because of the many guests who had come to the funeral.

"Lord," Martha greeted Jesus, with what might have been a tone of reproach, "if you had been here, my brother would not have died." She knew he could have come earlier. Lazarus was four days in the tomb. Jesus had delayed too long. "But even now," she said, "I know that if you ask God anything, he will give it to you."

It was apparent to the Apostles that she wanted Jesus to do again what he had done in Naim and in Capharnaum. But the man in Naim was only a few hours dead. And the girl in Capharnaum, the daughter of Jairus, had died just a few minutes before Jesus said to her, "Arise!" This was a much different case. Lazarus had died four days ago. His soul must be with the blessed of Abraham. And his body — it were best not to think of what had happened to his body.

"Your brother will rise," Jesus said gently.

"I know," Martha said, a trifle shrewishly. "He will rise at the resurrection, on the last day."

"I am the Resurrection," Jesus said to her. He said it as simply as he had said, "I am the Light of the world. . . . I am the Good Shepherd. . . . I and the Father are one."

"I am the Resurrection and the Life. He that believes in me, even though he be dead, shall live. And every one that lives and believes in me shall never die. Do you believe that?"

"Yes Lord," she said. "I believe you are the Christ, the Son of God, who has come into the world."

When she had said that she made him a bow, turned, and ran home to bid Mary come and greet him.

Jesus waited until Mary came. She came quickly, with a great many of the mourners following her. She threw herself at the beloved feet, weeping. She greeted him with the same words Martha had used. "Lord, if you had been here, my brother would not have died." She had no reproaches. There was such love in her, and such grief, and such utter trust, that Jesus was touched.

"Where have you laid him?" he asked.

And he wept!

Did Mary's tears give birth to his? Was he weeping for humanity in general, always so distressed and shocked, made helpless by the death of someone close and dear? Was he weeping for the dead who went so needlessly and heedlessly to hell? He was about to restore his friend Lazarus to life and health. Surely he did not weep for him.

The tomb was a cave, its entrance blocked by a stone. "Take away the stone," Jesus said. Martha would have interfered, Martha who was always busy about so many things that didn't matter. "Lord," she said, "by this time he stinks. He has been dead four days."

"Did I not tell you," Jesus rebuked her tenderly, "that if you had faith, you would see the glory of God?"

Martha, not knowing how to answer, stepped aside; and several strong men moved the stone from the entrance of the tomb.

"Father," Jesus said, "I thank you that you have heard me. Yet I know you always hear me. I speak aloud that the people standing about may hear, and believe you have sent me."

Then, with a loud voice, he cried out: "Lazarus, come forth!"

The dead man could have heard a whisper, if it came from God. He could not have heard the voice of an ordinary man, no matter if it were a thousand times as loud as the voice of Jesus.

Nobody moved. Every man and woman standing there looked as dead and rigid as the stones about them. No one made any sort of sound. No one, in the terrible suspense, even dared to breathe.

Nobody moved but the man four days dead, bound in linens and snug in his tomb. He came forth at the call of Jesus, the grave clothes clinging to him, giving him the look and the shape of a ghost.

Somehow his absent soul had returned to him. Somehow his corrupted and stinking flesh had been restored to normal firmness and fresh smell. Somehow his dead hands and feet moved with life.

"Unwrap him," Jesus said. His voice brought life to the spectators. They sprang to Lazarus, stripped the linens from him, put a cloak around his strong young naked body, and gave him to his sisters.

Mary, after she had embraced her brother, went back to Jesus.

"Lord," she said, "there were tears in your eyes. Or maybe I imagined that, for my own eyes were streaming when I first looked upon your face."

"Peace," Jesus soothed her. "Tears speak for us when we have no words. Your brother lives. But he shall die again, in my Father's appointed time. We shall all die in the body, for we are mortal; yet the spirit shall not die."

"Not you, Lord," Mary cried. "Surely not you!"

"The good shepherd lays down his life for his sheep," Jesus answered. "I go to Jerusalem soon — that my sheep may not perish."

Mary flinched and paled. A look of terror came into her eyes and vanished. Protests rose to her lips. She swallowed them down bravely.

"Lord, help me to say 'Thy will be done'!" she begged. "Help me to be like your mother, Mary — as much as I can be like her. Help me to bear this bitterest of all bitter secrets."

She saw that Lazarus was trying to force his way through crowds of curious people to thank Jesus for his life, and she was glad, for it gave her an opportunity to run away.

She fled back to the house. She walked out of it a few minutes later, and turned her steps toward Jerusalem, the great city just over the top of the hill. She walked swiftly, her eyes burning as though with a high fever, the taste of salt in her mouth. She walked through the marketplaces in the city until she found the stall she sought. And there she exchanged her last jewel, a pearl, for an alabaster jar filled with spikenard.

The merchant almost dropped the pearl when he saw it.

"One seldom looks upon a beauty such as this," he said, "and you can part with it for this?"

"The jar is beautiful too," Mary said, scarcely looking at it, "and the ointment is precious, is it not?"

"Indeed the jar is beautiful," the merchant agreed. "And it was carved by a great Greek artist. It is genuine Egyptian stone.

It is an exquisite material. And the nard is genuine. But, as I am an honest man, and no thief, I tell you this pearl would buy a dozen alabaster jars. Even two dozen."

"The ointment is for a Man I love," Mary said simply. "It is for his burial. And if I had all the pearls in the world, I would give them to you for this jar and the nard within it."

There was a man with Martha, she saw, when she returned to Bethany. His back was to her, but she knew by his beautiful linen clothes with the long fringes, that he was a Pharisee. And she guessed his identity before he turned to see who had come in. She was right. It was Simon the Leper. He had been a boyhood friend of Lazarus; and he had been among the mourners when Jesus arrived. Had that been just a little while ago?

He recognized her but pretended not to see her. He turned back to Martha, arguing with her about some dinner he had arranged. Martha had not yet made up her mind. Mary listened a few moments. It was to be a dinner for Lazarus, and also for Jesus and his Apostles. Simon wanted Martha to prepare a meal and serve it. No wonder Martha hesitated. How was it that a Pharisee wished to invite Jesus to dine beneath his roof? Martha kept making excuses.

"Ask him why he wants Jesus for his guest." Mary said to her. Simon started to turn toward her, changed his mind.

"Why?" Martha asked.

"Why what?" Simon demanded.

"Why do you want Jesus for your guest?"

"Because I admire him, in a way," Simon answered slowly, and with seeming honesty. "Since men began to talk, no man has ever said the things he says. I do not agree with anything he says, yet I love the way he says it. He hates the rich and the powerful. But that is natural, for he is but a carpenter, and from Nazareth at that; a man brought up in bitter poverty and hatred for authority. But what a wonderful way he puts it! It will be easier for a camel to pass through the eye of a needle, he says, than for a rich man to go to heaven. Now those are the words of a genius, an artist, a profound philosopher. He is a great man, this Jesus, though he would wreck the world in order to rebuild it in his own fashion."

"He does not hate the rich," Mary cried out. "He hates no one, he loves everybody. Even you. When one of his disciples asked him about the camel and the needle's eye, Jesus said nothing was impossible for God. He could send an army of rich men, mounted on the tallest of camels, and riding twenty abreast, straight through the eye of the smallest needle in the world."

Again Simon ignored her. "And I owe him something," he said to Martha. "I was a leper once. You knew that, didn't you?"

"Oh yes," Martha said, "Of course. Did we not leave food for you every week — Mary and Lazarus and I?"

Simon was silent a long time. "I was a leper, like all the other lepers," he said softly. "I cried 'unclean, unclean,' when anyone came near. I rang a bell. I ate the food friends left for me. I saw Jesus and asked him to make me clean. 'Be you clean,' he said. 'Go show yourself to the priest.' I ran to a priest, a friend of my father's. He told me I was clean, and I wept for joy. But the priest warned me not to be too joyful. Leprosy had many forms, he explained. Sometimes a man had a disease that looked like leprosy but was not, a disease that lasted but a short time — and was no more painful than pimples, for instance — and cured itself. I had been cured, the priest assured me, even before I begged Jesus to have pity on me."

"So you didn't bother to go back to Jesus and thank him," Mary said.

Simon pretended he had heard nothing. "My sores had disappeared," he said to Martha. "I saw this in the home of the priest. But I hadn't looked at myself for months before that. Sometimes sores dry up without your knowing it. I thought it

might embarrass the Prophet if I went back to him. And — and
I thought he was a sham. Good. Well-meaning. But a fraud. I
went back to my family. My father was dead. I was the only
heir. People still call me Simon the Leper. Perhaps they always
will."

"You hate Jesus, don't you?" Mary asked him. He swung
around, anger making him forget that this woman was a mere
sinner, one not to be looked upon.

Martha, thinking to appease him, touched his shoulder. "Very
well," she said. "I will come. I know what Jesus likes. And
Lazarus too, of course. I will help you, Simon."

Simon glared his fill at Mary. He had loved her once. She
would never let him touch her, even when she was a child. But
he had loved her ardently. Now he hated her. But he must not
even acknowledge she was alive. He was a Pharisee. She was a
wanton sinner.

After Martha had left, Mary began to brush and comb her
hair. She looked carefully at her scanty wardrobe — which once
had been so magnificent. She selected a modest robe. She put
on the earrings her mother had given her, perfumed her hands
and her hair, covered her head with a shawl, and went to Simon's
house, carrying the alabaster jar. The night was dark; and it
had begun to rain, a fine, thin cold rain.

The dinner was almost over. Jesus and Lazarus were close
together, reclining on their couches. Mary saw them at once.
She took off the shawl and handed it to Martha as she passed.

The room hushed. Men stirred, turned, stared. Seldom had
they seen a woman so beautiful. Mary knelt behind her Lord,
opening the precious jar. She kissed his feet; and the tears came,
in spite of her. She washed his feet with those tears, then used
her hair as a cloth to dry them. She rubbed the spikenard into
them, letting its scent pervade the room.

Simon sneered. "I was right," he thought. "The Man is an

obvious fraud, great though he is! Otherwise he would not permit this woman to defile him with her presence."

Jesus beckoned to him, and he rose, wondering. "Simon," Jesus began, "I have something to say to you."

"Say it, Rabbi," Simon said, trying to keep the odor of the spikenard from defiling his nostrils, and hoping to fly after a word or two from this impostor.

"A certain man had two debtors," Jesus said. "One owed him a trifling sum; the other owed much more. Neither could pay. So he forgave them both. Tell me, which of the two loved him the more?"

"The one whom he forgave more," Simon said. Jesus nodded. "That is right. Now, you see this woman? When I came into your house you gave me no water for my feet. But she has washed them with kisses and with tears, and dried them with the splendor of her hair. You gave me no kiss of greeting. She has covered my feet with kisses. You did not anoint my head with oil, as a host usually does. But see how she anoints my feet! Wherefore I say to you, many sins are forgiven her, because she has loved much."

Mary raised herself, still weeping. What ointment was left in the jar she rubbed gently into the hair of her Lord's head. And, as she left the room, she broke the jar — that it might never know a lesser love, be put to a less noble use.

Judas Iscariot, who had risen as though to wrest the jar from Mary's hands before she destroyed it, sank back onto his couch, snarling and scowling "That is spikenard," he said. "Precious stuff. It might have been sold for a great deal of money."

"Let her alone," Jesus bade him. "The poor you have always with you. Me you will not always have. She came to anoint me for my burial. And I say to you that wheresoever the Gospel shall be preached in the whole world, that which she has done will be told in memory of her."

Mary went directly home, through the rain. Martha and Simon were there, evidently waiting for her.

"What in the world possessed you?" Martha began, but Simon wouldn't let her talk. He stood facing Mary. His face was a puzzle to her.

"I want you to look down on someone lower than yourself," Simon said, "someone really low. A host who does not know how to treat such a guest as the Prophet Jesus! I am dirt beneath your feet. Trample me!"

"You would do something for me?" Mary asked.

"Try me."

"Bring his mother here. She has a little house in Capharnaum. It looks on the sea. It is easy to find. Everybody knows Mary, the mother of Jesus. Ask the first man or woman you meet. Bring her here, to this house. As soon as you can."

"But the Man is going soon to his death," Simon objected.

"He is," Mary said. "And I have promised his mother I would let her know in time."

"She would be with him? She would see him die?"

"She is that sort of woman."

Martha protested. "You are out of your mind, Mary. We must clean this filthy house first. We must lime it. We must rearrange the furniture. We must . . ."

"I will bring her within the week," Simon promised.

There were voices outside. Jesus was speaking to someone, probably Lazarus. Simon took two strides past Mary, who was near the door, brushing against her without thinking of any contamination. He confronted Jesus and Lazarus. They were standing together, looking up at the starlit sky. The rain had stopped, but two black streams were gurgling down the side of the hill, and a half-moon was wrestling with a pale gray cloud.

"Lord," Simon said, "I have something to say to you."

"Say it," Jesus said, gesturing for Lazarus to go inside.

"You give a man no choice," Simon said. "You say do this, do that, and there is no arguing with you. Either you are right and all the rest of the world is wrong. Or you are wrong and the world is right. I must love my enemies, you say. I must do good to those who hate me. I do not love my enemies. I do not even love my friends. If I do good to anyone, he will expect more and more good from me. Lay not up riches, you tell me, for moths and rust to consume, or thieves to steal. You tell me to sell what I have and give to the poor, then follow you — to a cross on a hill. I cannot take these words. No sane man can take them. Shall I turn my cheek to one who has given me a blow? Not I. I shall have a servant run him through or set my dogs on him. Shall I be meek, to possess the land? Not I. Shall I be poor in spirit, pure in heart? Not I. Shall I be concerned that justice is given all, even those I know not? No. Shall I bother to make peace between people who hate? Do not ask me that. And shall I let myself be persecuted for your sake? You bring me death, Lord. Death to everything I am, everything I have, everything I have been. I know who you are. I knew this morning. I know that any man can cancel life; but only God can cancel death. But I would not admit it. For it would cancel my life. I admit it now because I have to. There is no choice.

"My life was built on rules and rituals as rigid and dead and dry as polyps in a coral island. But I was comfortable in that life. I am rich. I am respected. I have nothing to do with the vulgar and the common and the poor. Why did you not let me alone? What is such as I to you?"

Abruptly he threw himself into the mud at Jesus' feet and began to sob as though he were in pain. "Lord," he begged, "let me, too, wash away my sins with the eyes you have opened. Why should a woman love you so much, and I so little, when it is I who owe you the more?"

Jesus bent down and whispered: "Simon, come forth!"

CHAPTER XXV

There is little more to tell and little more to "make up" as we go along the highway of the life of Jesus. There is only the last week of his life to reconstruct from the materials of the Gospels and the stuff supplied by the love in our minds and hearts.

That week revealed the awfulness of the world's pride, and the fanatic hatred it bore God. It also showed the unlimited humility of the Most High and his boundless love for men, his most stubborn and willful creatures. It was a week stained with the greatest crime in human history, and starred with its greatest blessing.

It was Lucifer who sped the week to its appalling end. The devil had been one of the most interested spectators at the tomb of Lazarus. He had suffered agonies of frustration and despair when Jesus raised his voice and the dead man came stumbling out of the bed meant for his eternal sleep. Lucifer had known intense fear; and he had prostrated himself like all the other angels in heaven and in hell, for he knew that Father, Son, and Holy Ghost had given a command.

In that moment he realized that if Jesus was not the very Son of God, he was, at the least, the greatest of all the prophets God had ever sent to earth, and the most powerful of his ambassadors. And it seemed to his angelic mind that mankind must also recognize Jesus as the messenger, the agent, the sacred Word of God; and that men would, therefore, abandon all worldly ideas of right and wrong to follow the teachings of their Lord.

His intellect could not, at first, entertain the idea that men, having free will, could defy God, knowing he was God; could disobey him, seeing him face to face; could actually hate him, being aware of his divinity. Then he remembered Judas, and he was comforted. Judas knew that Jesus was either God or God's best friend. Yet he was ready to betray him.

And there were others on whom the dark angel could rely. The high priests, Annas and Caiphas, were, of course, among these. They were sterling characters, these two. Annas loved power and money. Caiphas loved power and money and Caiphas. And he hated not only Jesus, but everybody else. Caiphas hated everybody because everybody called him Caiphas, which means "the belcher." They had forgotten his real name. They wouldn't recognize it as his if they heard it. Everybody knew him only as "the belcher." He had belched hatred, naturally, on all — but especially on Jesus. Annas and Caiphas! Friends in need; friends indeed. Lucifer must use them now in this crisis.

The free will that permitted a man to place himself and his wants above the love and the law of God, could also let him humble himself that he might love and worship God. Free will could make a saint of every man and woman on the earth. Everyone, if he knew that Jesus was God's true representative, might decide to be a saint. That must not happen!

A few months ago Jesus had had uncounted thousands of followers. He was their champion, their hero, their hope. They wanted to make him their leader, their king, their deliverer. They didn't know, then — though they should have known, because of his tremendous miracles — that He was God's living Word. But now, after this affair with Lazarus, they would suspect the truth. And they would come back to him, bringing hosts of friends!

Therefore, it seemed logical to Lucifer, the sooner Jesus died the better it would be for hell. He hurried away from the tomb to talk to Judas and to the high priests.

"This is your opportunity, Judas. Your Master has gone too far, raising up the dead in defiance of nature and the wishes of the high priests. When a man is dead he should be left in peace. Go to the priests and offer them your Lord. They will pay money for him."

Judas refused to heed this temptation; not immediately, though. It had made him think. And Lucifer read his thoughts.

"Don't be afraid," he said. "Nothing will happen to him. You have seen him escape from angry men before. He vanishes magically. The high priests will pay you handsomely and send men to seize him. All you have to do is point him out. When they try to take him, he will disappear again. But you will have your silver, and the goodwill of the priests. When you declare yourself the Messiah, they will back you. You can make a good thing of this. The oftener you betray your friend, the more silver it will bring — and the more influence you will gain with those who count. Begin now."

Judas shook his head. But after he had been publicly rebuked at the dinner given by Simon the Leper, and while he was seething with anger at his Master, he visited the high priests and began to bargain with them. They settled on thirty pieces of silver.

When Jesus rode into Jerusalem on the ass's colt — the first man to sit upon it — Lucifer joined in the excitement of the crowds. He looked upon those spreading their cloaks upon the road, and those waving branches of palms, and those shouting Hosannas, and actually felt pleased — as pleased as the devil could ever be. He made himself believe he had engineered this bit of business — and that the crowds were applauding him for his cunning. Jesus had ridden into Lucifer's trap, and he would not escape!

He listened with tolerance to the cries of "Blessed is he who comes as our king in the name of the Lord. . . . Lo, the king of Israel! . . . Hosanna in the highest!" Within the week, he told himself, these same people would be crying; "Crucify him, crucify him; his blood be on our heads!"

One of the Pharisees stepped out of the crowd and angrily told Jesus to rebuke his noisy disciples.

"I tell you," Jesus said mildly, "if they were silent, the very stones would cry out."

The next moment he was weeping over the fate of Jerusalem. The time would come, he predicted, when enemies would dig a trench around the city, and besiege it from every side. They would beat it flat to the ground — and all the children in it — and would not leave a stone upon a stone! Because it had not let God shower his graces on it!

Lucifer rejoiced when he learned that Jerusalem would be destroyed. He was not only going to commit the perfect crime, he was going to collect abundant interest from it. He rejoiced even more — in his own hellish way — when he heard Jesus say:

"The hour has come for the Son of man to be glorified. . . . Unless the grain of wheat falls into the ground and dies, it remains alone. But if it dies, it brings forth much fruit. He who loves his life, loses it; and he who hates his life in this world, keeps it unto life everlasting."

The Man had come here, knowing he was to die. Furthermore, He was resigned to dying. He was a quitter, Lucifer thought, glad that he could feel some contempt for this lordly enemy. Was Jesus tired of the fight? He would be more tired, Lucifer promised. He would be glad to die before Lucifer finished with him.

"Now my soul is troubled," Jesus said to Andrew and Philip. "What shall I say? 'Father, save me from this hour'?"

No. He would not say that. "Father, glorify thy name," he said. A voice answered him. A voice out of heaven. And Lucifer fell prostrate onto the stones, as frightened as he had been when Jesus was baptized.

"I have glorified it," the voice answered, "and will glorify it again."

Many people heard the voice. Some thought it was an angel. Some thought they had heard nothing but thunder. Jesus told them the voice had spoken for their sakes. The world was being condemned by heaven; the prince of the world would be cast out of his kingdom; and he, Jesus, would be lifted up from the earth. That is, he would be lifted on a cross. And he would draw all things to himself.

Lucifer, when he could, crawled away; and busied himself perfecting his plans for that "lifting up."

Jesus, preparing for death, lived every day to the full. He taught daily in the Temple. He healed the sick and the maimed, the blind and the deaf and the lame. He humbled the Pharisees and Sadducees who sought to argue against him. And he preached continually of love.

"Master," one of the Scribes asked him, "which is the great commandment in the Law?"

Jesus answered without any hesitation; "Thou shalt love the Lord thy God with thy whole heart, and with thy whole soul, and with thy whole mind." He added; "This is the greatest, and the first, commandment. And the second is like it. Thou shalt love thy neighbor as thyself. On these two commandments depend the whole Law and the Prophets."

The astonished Scribe exclaimed, "Well answered!" To which Jesus replied, "You are not far from the kingdom of God."

On Thursday morning, "the first day of the Unleavened Bread," Jesus sent Peter and John into Jerusalem to prepare the Passover feast. "You will meet a man carrying a pitcher of water," Jesus told them. "Follow him. He will show you a large upstairs room. Make things ready there."

A man carrying a pitcher of water? Carrying water was a woman's chore. A man never did such a thing. But the Apostles found a man carrying a pitcher of water. They followed him. He led them to the room. It was large and airy. It was high above the tomb of David. They made it ready.

Jesus was ready.

Caiphas was ready. He had taken charge of the Sanhedrin and all those opposed to Jesus. There had been much confusion in their ranks when it was learned that "the Prophet" had wakened a dead man and brought him out of his tomb in his death clothes. Some, asserting that Jesus must be divine, sought to make their peace with him. Others were more than ever determined to be rid of him.

"We should kill Lazarus," some said.

"That's a crazy idea," others argued. "Jesus would bring him back to life the second time. Then where would we be?"

The majority realized that Jesus was ruining them and all they stood for. He might or might not be God, or a dear friend of God's, yet he must not be permitted to interfere with their established customs and beliefs. Was he of more importance than they and theirs?

He was making many converts. Not only that; he was also stirring up the crowds. Pretty soon he would have all the people with him again. Then he would establish his kingdom, about which he talked so much. Or he would attempt to establish it. And that would offend the Roman eagles!

Caiphas and Annas gathered the chief priests and the Pharisees into a council. And it was there that Caiphas shouted: "It is expedient for us that one man die for the people, instead of the whole nation perishing."

Caiphas was inspired to utter those words. He was the high priest that year, and the Holy Spirit spoke through him, prophesying that Jesus was to die "for the nation"; and that he might unite the scattered children of God.

And the high priest's army was ready. Judas would give Caiphas the place and the time. He would also identify his Victim with a friendly kiss.

The soldiers would make the capture. There would be a trial. The Prisoner would be provoked into saying something that might be termed blasphemous. Or, if that failed, any number of witnesses could be called to testify against him. It didn't matter at all what they said. They were sure to convict him.

Caiphas, despite the irregularity of the trial, and the way it would be conducted, would find justification — he was sure — for condemning the Prisoner to death. But it was illegal to put any man to death. It was illegal because the Romans made the law. Caiphas had to have the help of Pontius Pilate.

"Render unto Caesar the things that are Caesar's" Jesus had once said, "and to God the things that are God's." He had been talking to Pharisees who asked if it was lawful to pay tribute to the Roman emperor — and who had sought to entrap him into saying something that would cause him trouble. Caiphas remembered that. Pilate, if he proved stubborn — and he might, since he hated the Jews so venomously — must be made to render unto Caesar the judgment and punishment of this Man who claimed that he was God. He might refuse, at first. He probably would refuse. But he could be handled by a clever use of Caesar's name. Pilate would nail Jesus to the cross. In Caesar's name! Render indeed unto Caesar!

The cross was ready too.

CHAPTER XXVI

As the Passover approached, Jerusalem throbbed with a pious and solemn gaiety — as though it listened to the music of heavenly harps. Yet where Jesus and his Apostles walked, the faces of men showed little happiness. He who had been set for the fall and the resurrection of many in Israel, and for a sign that would be contradicted, was a disturbance, a crisis, an embarrassment, and a danger. He was One to be avoided.

Everyone who saw him, even for the first time, recognized him. Some, including those who once had loved him, pretended not to see him. They might see again the love and pity that always rode at anchor in the serene harbor of his eyes. Others squeezed themselves against the nearest wall as he approached, wishing they could pass through it. Or they tried to take advantage of passing camels or well-laden asses or groups of Roman soldiers, to hide from the tidal waves of anger that sometimes smashed through that same harbor to overwhelm and wash away hypocrisy and pride.

One man spat contemptuously in the direction of the Messiah, then looked slyly at a nearby priest, as though to seek approval and applause. A few hailed Jesus with evident delight. One boldly cried a blessing on him. But these were the exceptions. Jerusalem felt that Jesus, since he had restored life to a corpse rotting in its tomb, had the power of God in him. But the power Jerusalem feared and respected was the power of the Pharisees and Scribes, the masters of Israel.

The narrow, sloping streets were so filled with pilgrims it was difficult to walk through them. The Apostles wondered idly how many people the city held. They had heard that the seven thousand priests in the Temple had already slaughtered more than two hundred thousand lambs. That would give one an idea of the people who would celebrate the Pasch — if one were good at figures. Judas could calculate the number; but nobody wanted to ask him. He was in one of his sullen moods today.

They could have asked Jesus to make a guess. But he seemed withdrawn, lost in some mystic meditation.

"I doubt that he's entirely happy," Thomas thought. "He expects to die here." Three times Jesus had said he would be delivered to his enemies in this city and would be put to death. He would be "lifted up." Thomas also remembered Jesus' remark to some friendly men in Galilee. They had told him to beware of Herod. "Go tell that fox," Jesus bade them, "that I will continue for a time to cure the sick and the afflicted, to cast out devils, and to preach the kingdom of God. When I finish, I shall go to Jerusalem. It cannot be that a prophet perish outside Jerusalem." Even now Thomas felt the divine irony in those words.

He doubted the priests would wait. They would kill him as quickly — and as quietly — as possible. They would not think of delaying his murder until the feast was ended. It wouldn't end until the eighth day after the Sabbath. They would try to do it today, tonight, certainly tomorrow. Thomas still hoped, and feared, to die with him.

Jesus did not have to guess. He knew. This night, after the supper with his Apostles, he would be sold to his enemies.

Tomorrow he would die. So be it. The time had been chosen, long long ago, by his Father.

The Passover commemorated the flight of the angel of death and the exodus of the children of Israel. The angel had visited all the homes of the Egyptians; and in every dwelling place he had slain the firstborn son. He had passed over the houses of the Jews, doing no harm in any of them; for they had been marked with the blood of a lamb, which was sprinkled on the lintels over their doors.

"Behold the Lamb of God who taketh away the sins of the world!"

Jesus the firstborn and only-begotten Son of God, would now be the victim of the angel of death. He would go like a lamb to the slaughter, without protest, without a struggle. His death would release the world of sinners from the heavy debt they owed the Lord, the debt they could never pay without his help.

The children of Israel ate their lamb hurriedly, standing, everyone dressed for travel, the men with staves in their hands. They ate it with unleavened bread and bitter herbs. And they sipped a red wine with it. Hundreds of thousands of their descendants would feast in similar fashion during these holy days, that the mercy and love of the Most High might be recalled and cherished.

The blood of the Lamb of God would be sprinkled on the lintels of thousands of millions of doors throughout the centuries to come, and it would save the children of God from the angel of damnation. Every drop of his blood would be shed to bless the earth. His blood and his flesh would nourish and sustain the world from generation unto generation until time should be no more.

In spite of the dense crowds, Jesus and his ten Apostles arrived at the upper room at the appointed time. Peter and John had everything ready. The Twelve went to the couches arranged around the U-shaped table, but with some bickering, a little jostling and shoving, and a few loud arguments. Each wanted to prove he was the greatest among the Twelve. Each wanted to recline as close to Jesus as he could. Jesus rebuked them, saying that he who was the greater among them should become a servant to the others. He chided Peter. The devil, he said, wanted "to sift him like wheat."

"But I," Jesus assured him, "have prayed for you, that your faith may not fail, and that, in time, you may be able to strengthen your brothers."

Peter shouted that his faith and loyalty were strong. He was ready, he asserted vehemently, to go to prison with Jesus and to death. Jesus shook his head sadly.

"Before the cock crows twice," he said, "you will have denied me thrice!"

He rose from his couch, removed his cloak, found a towel, poured water into a basin, and began to wash the Apostles' feet.

Lucifer, hovering near Judas, watched this spectacle with all his angelic powers of observation and attention. And wonder grew in him. And terror.

Assuming Jesus was God, this was a divine lesson in humility. And he might actually be God, for all Lucifer could prove to the contrary. He had said repeatedly that he was God, and the Son of God. "The Father and I are one. . . . Who sees me sees the Father. . . . Who receives me receives the One who sent me." He backed up this claim by walking on the sea, bidding the winds be still, casting out the wickedest of devils, and transforming a graveyard into something like a picnic grounds. He acted like God, though he was only the son of a carpenter. But then — maybe he *was* God! No. He was only the son of an ordinary couple, Joseph and Mary.

But say he was God. He was on his knees, like the lowest

slave, ministering to ordinary, unimportant, weak, quarrelsome, stupid men! He was washing their feet with divine patience, with care, even with reverence! That was the most astonishing thing of all — his reverence for these sinful creatures.

This was what he had meant by calling himself the good shepherd. He was tending his sheep. And he would die for any one of them. Lucifer knew that now. Every one of them, even Judas, had, to him, a value equal to every drop of blood pumping through him! Lucifer despaired of understanding this strange Man!

Peter protested when the Lord knelt before him. He thought of the time he had thrown himself before Jesus, in the boat, saying, "Depart from me, O Lord, for I am a sinful man." He felt he was still a sinful man, and that it was not right for Jesus to so demean himself.

"If I do not wash you," Jesus said mildly, "you will have no part with me." Immediately Peter changed his mind, saying, "Lord, wash not only my feet but my hands and face as well."

"After a bath," Jesus said, "one need only wash his feet and he is clean." He looked around then at the other Apostles. "You are clean," he said, "but not every one of you."

"Quiet!" Lucifer bade Judas. But Judas had had no intention of opening his mouth.

Eventually Jesus knelt before the man who was planning to betray Him. Lucifer's terror mounted. Suppose those miraculous hands worked some miracle of grace in Judas! What a blow that would be to hell! He perched himself on Judas' shoulder, that he might whisper instructions into his ear.

But he could do nothing, nor could he say anything; for this was a most fantastic situation!

Almighty God — again assuming Jesus had told the truth — was crouched at the feet of one he might be expected to despise. Incarnate Wisdom was ministering — with reverence and love

— to the meanest and most ignorant clod on earth! Infinite Mercy had lowered himself before human avarice and pride and petty malice. Divine Love had abased himself to serve a sinner who distrusted and hated him, and who, he knew, would soon betray him!

The humility and the forgiveness of God made Lucifer cry out, against his will, "Holy, Holy, Holy Lord God of Hosts!"

He was astonished that Judas said no word of any kind to his Master and his Lord. Nay. He was actually scandalized! For Judas not only was silent, he was even contemptuous and displeased!

"He thinks he is the equal, or even the superior, of Jesus," Lucifer discovered. "Jesus to him, is like a slave groveling at his dirty ankles, and trying to make up for his rudeness at Simon the Leper's dinner. That night Jesus had dared to reprimand Judas in public. Judas feels it is right that his Master should pay for that in public. Judas is hungry not only for a measure of revenge, but for some recognition of his abilities and talents. He wants Jesus to apologize to him, now, while he is kneeling so servilely there, and to implore his forgiveness. He actually expects it!

In Judas, Lucifer beheld an image of himself, and he hated the man then almost as much as he hated himself. He, the most beautiful of all the angels, had once sat as close to the Most High as Judas did now to Jesus. But Lucifer hadn't envied God as Judas envied Jesus. He had not felt equal to God. He had not felt superior to God.

Judas was indeed prepared to accept an apology. But not immediately. He would make Jesus wait. He would amuse himself with his humble Master, as a cat amused itself with a captured mouse.

Judas was a greater fool than Lucifer had fancied. If Jesus were God, he had chosen this dolt for a great place in his kingdom. Judas would rank as high as any archangel near the throne. He was abandoning the possibility of attaining that rank, so he could feed his spite, his hatred, his raging envy, and his ever growing greed for gold and power.

Judas had almost as much pride as Lucifer, Lucifer thought. Yet God had not damned him. And he might not damn him! It was so easy to see that Jesus actually loved this frightful, distorted, wretched, ridiculous, self-swelled sinner! He might even save him from hell!

What was there in men that God should love them so?

But he must save this sinner for himself, Lucifer determined.

"Good old Judas," he whispered. "Soft, docile, easily pleased old Judas! Nice old spongy Judas! Wet him with tears and wipe your greasy hands on him for everybody to see. Judas won't mind. The hands that sullied him can wring him dry again, with a mere twist of the wrists. Dependable, gullible, simple old Judas! Slap him hard and he turns the other cheek, as he was bidden. Maybe not so good as those fishmouthed louts from Galilee, but good enough to fetch and carry for the Master. Jesus will not ask your pardon, Judas. He has no further need of you. Nor you of him.

"Caiphas was right. Jesus is a deceiver. But you knew that. He claims to be poor; yet he gets himself bathed in the costliest of all costly ointments. Real spikenard! How long would it take you — or him — to earn or beg enough money to buy that stuff? He talks of purity too. But he lets a wanton weep all over him, and dry his tear-wet feet with her unbound hair! Imagine Caiphas in the presence of such a woman! Can you? A great man, Caiphas. A man you can trust. An important man. Straightforward. Honest. If he doesn't feel he can spare Jesus, he tells you so, to your face. And he offers an honest price. You will do well with Caiphas at your side."

In spite of all his wealth of flattery and sarcasm, Lucifer smelled failure. Judas was surely slipping forward into the mercy and love of God. Lucifer made a supreme effort.

"Jesus thinks you have a devil," he whispered. "He doesn't trust you. He's giving the purse to his pet, John. How do you like that? What will you do now? How will you eat? How will you drink? How will you attract the women? Do you think you can borrow money from your friend John?"

Judas stiffened. Lucifer relaxed.

When Jesus rose, without having made an effort to win back his angry Apostle's love, Judas told himself he was glad he had not softened. He set himself for the task ahead.

"Now," Jesus said, returning to his couch that he might resume the interrupted supper, "do you know what I have done? I, your Lord and Master, in washing your feet, have set you an example. You ought to wash the feet of one another. As I have done, so do you also . . . for the servant is not greater than his Lord, nor the apostle than him who sent him. If you know these things and act accordingly, you will be blessed."

Then solemnly he said: "Amen, amen, I say to you, one of you will betray me. One of you eating with me now."

The Apostles, excited and shocked, and suspicious of one another, began to ask, "Is it I?" Peter signaled to John, bidding him ask the Lord who it was. John, leaning back on his couch so that his head rested on the bosom of Jesus, asked, "Who is it?"

"He for whom I dip the bread," Jesus answered, thrusting a morsel of unleavened bread into the dish of bitter herbs. "He to whom I give it."

"Is it I?" Judas asked, leaning across the table. Jesus put the bread into his hands, a common way of showing affection to a guest. "You have said it," he replied. "The Son of man departs, as it has been decreed, but woe to him by whom he is betrayed. It were better for that man that he had not been born."

Lucifer, badly frightened again, for fear of the effect those words might have, bade Judas rise and go. "This is your hour," he whispered. "Take full advantage of it." Obediently, Judas bowed to Jesus and started out of the room. Jesus gave him one last chance to save himself.

"What you do," he said, "do quickly."

Judas was startled, knowing now, beyond all doubting, that Jesus was aware of the plot against him. He felt a strange impulse to throw himself down and weep. But the thought of asking pardon of anyone, especially Jesus, repelled him. And bending the knee in confession was impossible to him. He hardened his heart. Jesus had been spying on him, he told himself. This was unforgivable! This must be avenged!

"Woe to me?" Judas thought. "Rather, woe to you, Rabbi. It will be you who will be sorry you were born. Caiphas will not be as gentle with you as I would be, were I in his place. And do not think you will play one of your tricks and vanish tonight when I come. When I kiss you for the soldiers, I will hold you for them."

Lucifer knew a moment of petty triumph. He had planned the the crime. It was really a tremendous crime, a perfect crime. But Judas would get the credit for it. And Caiphas. And many others. He was even amused. Judas was studying the black sky and the full moon rising from its hem, as though he were afraid he might be struck by lightning.

Yet Lucifer also trembled with fears. Suppose this man he was about to kill were really the Son of God — what would God do to him?

CHAPTER XXVII

Peter and John kept their knowledge of Judas to themselves. The other Apostles thought it odd that Judas should leave when he did, but supposed Jesus had sent him on an errand. They didn't miss him, for they were absorbed in the things Jesus was doing and saying.

Never had he greeted them so warmly as he had tonight. Never had he so plainly shown his love, nor talked about it. "I have desired greatly to eat this Passover with you," he said, "before I suffer." It would be the last he would eat until it was "fulfilled in the kingdom of God." And the wine would be the last he would sip until the kingdom had come.

They did not understand his words. They knew only that there were extremes of sadness and joy and defeat and triumph in him which no man could weigh or measure. But they listened with attention.

He seemed concerned about Judas; but his face shone, after the Apostle had gone out into the night, and he said, with jubilance: "Now is the Son of man glorified, and God is glorified in him." Then he gave the Eleven "a new commandment." They were to love one another, even as he had loved them. By this would all men know they were his disciples: that they loved one another.

And never had he been so intimate with them. "Let not your hearts be troubled," he said. "You believe in God, believe also in me. In my Father's house there are many mansions. Were it not so, I would have told you. . . . I go to prepare a place for you. You know where I go. You know the way."

But they didn't know the way, Thomas said.

"I am the way," Jesus explained. "I am the way and the truth and the life. No one comes to the Father but through me."

Philip asked to be shown the Father.

"I have been a long time with you, Philip," Jesus said, sighing, "and you do not know me? Who sees me sees the Father. . . . He who believes in me will do the things I do; and even greater things, because I am going to the Father, and whatever you ask in my name I will do, that the Father may be glorified in the Son. . . . If you love me, keep my commandments."

Divine Love was saying farewell to men who were dear to him despite the fact that they had learned so little from him. Divine Wisdom was making his last will and testament, appointing them his heirs — them and theirs through all the generations yet to come. He would send them the Holy Ghost, he promised. "Another Advocate," he called him, and "the Spirit of Truth." He, the Holy Ghost, would dwell with them. He would dwell in them. No, Jesus would not leave them orphans. He had already provided for them. And he himself would come for them — some day.

"If anyone love me, he will keep my word, and my Father will love him. And we will come to him and make our abode with him."

He gave his peace. And he gave himself, the Perfect Gift.

He blessed a piece of bread and broke it. He gave the pieces to his loved ones, saying "take and eat. This is my body!"

They ate the bread, wondering. So this was what he had meant when he said they must eat his flesh to have eternal life! How

simple it was, after all! They had forgotten he was God, and that
nothing is impossible to God. Of course he could take a common
bit of bread and turn it into his body. And wasn't it like him to
choose bread, the most common of all foods?

It looked like bread. It had the smell and the feel and the
taste and the shape of bread. But it was the body of the Lord.
They knew this, for he had said so.

"Do this," he said, "in remembrance of me!"

He took up a cup of wine, blessed it, and gave it to them,
saying: "Drink this, all of you; for this is my blood of the new
convenant, which shall be shed for many, unto the forgiveness
of sins."

They accepted the wine in the same holy silence that had
greeted his gift of the bread. It looked like wine. It had the color
of wine, the aroma, the taste, the tingle. But it was the blood of
Jesus, the blood of God.

"Do this," Jesus said, "in remembrance of me!"

He was pleased with their faith in him. Blessed were they
because they believed. But blessed indeed would those be,
throughout all the years to come, until the consummation of the
world, who had not seen Jesus, nor listened to him, nor lived
in his time, yet believed in him and sought his flesh to eat, his
blood to drink!

Blind faith would look upon his compassionate face when
consecrated bread was distributed at the altar. Deaf love would
hear his voice speaking plainly; would hear the beating of his
heart. John would not be the only one to lay his head upon the
Savior's bosom. Human weakness would swallow God's own
power.

His heart, Jesus knew, would be stilled on the morrow; and
a lance would bring blood and water enough out of it to wash
away all the sins of the world. Yet, after he had risen from the
tomb, the heart would beat again, as steadily as before, in his

glorified body — and it could be pierced, then, only with the lance of human love.

He spoke about his Mystical Body, knowing they would not understand; knowing also that the Holy Ghost would explain it to even the least astute among them. He was the vine. They were the branches. Every branch was expected to bear fruit, much fruit. His Father, who owned the vineyard, would prune the vine, cutting away the branches that were barren and cast them out to be burned; cleaning the fruitful branches so they might produce more fruit.

Every once in a while he reminded them he was soon to die. "You will all be scandalized this night because of me; for it is written, 'I will smite the Shepherd, and the sheep will be scattered.' But after I have risen I will go before you into Galilee." And over and over again he told them of his love, and bade them love one another. "These things I have spoken, that my joy may be in you, and your joy be made full. . . . Love one another as I have loved you. . . . Greater love than this no man has, that he lay down his life for his friends. . . . You are my friends if you do the things I command you. . . . You have not chosen me; I have chosen you." And every so often he gave them a word of comfort. "You will weep and lament, but the world will rejoice. You will be sorrowful, but your sorrow will be turned into joy. . . . I will see you again and your hearts shall rejoice, and your joy no one shall take from you."

After reciting a last hymn, they went out of the room, down the stone stairway, into the city, and through it to the Mount of Olives. Jesus talked to them as they walked. The city still pulsed with excitement and exultation, but the streets were quieter than they had been earlier that day — though there were drunken men and loudmouthed soldiers, some of them singing ribald songs, disturbing the peace of the night.

"Sit here and pray," Jesus said when he had reached the

garden of Gethsemani, the place of the olive press. He beckoned three of them not to sit down, but to follow him. These were his favorites, Peter, James, and John. He led them a few paces from the others, saying, "My soul is sorrowful even unto death." He looked at the earth and found a spot that was free of stones. "Wait here," he said, "and watch. And pray that you may not enter into temptation." He walked a few steps forward, and fell on the ground.

Once these three had seen him shining in glory, with Moses and Elias on either side of him. And they had heard the voice from heaven saying: "This is my beloved Son, in whom I am well pleased; hear ye him." Now they beheld him writhing in agony, and crying to his Father with agonizing words. This time his Father did not seem to hear or heed him. "Father," he begged, "if it be possible, let this chalice pass from me. Nevertheless, not as I will, but as you will."

Pilgrims had pitched their tents among the olive trees higher up. All the way to the top of the slope their fires gleamed and their lanterns shone, starring the hillside. The place where Jesus lay was enclosed by tall, tough, gnarled, and twisted olive trees; and was lighted only by the rays of the bright full moon. The Apostles could see that blood was oozing from his forehead and his cheeks, with his sweat. They shuddered. They wished that, somehow, they could help him. They clutched one another tightly like frightened children. And they watched — for a little time.

Many writers describe Jesus as a weakling, a cringing coward, a man so sensitive to pain he dreaded even the thought of it. They disregard the fact that he had promised his followers little else but pain, privations, persecution, imprisonment, and death; and that he could not possibly have sought to escape the fate he offered them. He must set his saints an example of fortitude and patience. He must show them how to suffer. It is the writers themselves, not Jesus, who shrink from the whip and the thorns and the nails and the cross. The same writers make him, at times, just a gingerbread Jesus. They water the wine of his forceful and stirring and intoxicating words. And they sugarcoat the harsh medicine of his commandments.

His agony was not caused by any sort of fear. It was born of revulsion of body and soul. The time had come for him to accept responsibility for our sins, that he might expiate them. One who intends to pay the debts of a friend must regard those debts as his own. He must at least learn what he can about them — their number, their nature, their magnitude or trifling unimportance — and the circumstances under which they were contracted, no matter how shameful those circumstances might have been. Jesus, about to redeem mankind, must look over the sins of mankind, see the penalties they merited — with interest compounded from the moment Eve pressed her lovely teeth against the skin of a forbidden apple, and thus bought original sin for all the human race — and, in a manner of speaking, make those sins his own! He must lie wallowing in the pigpen of the centuries that had passed, and the centuries to come, sick with the stench of sin, and shamed beyond all telling.

He knew that one drop of his blood, freely and lovingly offered, would be accepted by his Father as full payment. He knew that in his circumcision he had shed enough blood to redeem a thousand worlds. He knew also that too large a section of mankind would not be impressed by these facts.

He knew, alas, that it would not be too impressed with his complete oblation of himself.

There was a sense of failure in him, as well as the feeling of horror and shame. Many many souls would go to hell in spite of him! Not even God could save them from themselves!

He groaned aloud. He pulled himself up from the ground and knelt. The watching trio saw an angel strengthening him; yet they noted he was still weak, still suffering. The bloody sweat had clotted his eyebrows, his mustache, his beard. It had spotted his robe and stained the rocks and the earth about him.

The sins of the early centuries had been so dreadful that his Father had poured down rain for forty days and forty nights, until all life on the earth was ended, save what was contained in the Ark. And there had been later sins that cried to heaven for swift and frightful vengeance. Idolatries that had opened the earth and buried sinners alive. Lusts that had brought fire and brimstone down from heaven to burn entire cities. Wars and raids and ravages and rapes that had led the Almighty to slaughter armies. Pride and covetousness and anger and willful disobedience and stubborn opposition to the divine will that had brought terror to earth, plagues to men and beasts, and dry rot or strange diseases to growing fields of grain.

These sins, in his agony, Jesus assumed. And when he had acknowledged them as "his own," to be paid in full, he sought the comradeship and comfort of his friends, men of goodwill and warm affection.

They had shut their eyes against the suffering of their Lord. They had sought escape, in sleep, from the sight of it, from the knowledge that it existed. And the brightness of the angel had dazzled them and gave them further cause to keep their eyes closed. And they were tired, and the ground was soft, and it was night, and the air was fragrant, and, somewhere up the tree-studded slope, groups of pilgrims were softly singing hymns. They had, naturally, drifted into sleep.

Jesus woke them, and let them see he was disappointed in them.

"Could you not watch one hour with me?" he asked. "Watch and pray, that you may not enter into temptation."

Yet, in his tenderness and compassion, he found an excuse for them: "The spirit indeed is willing, but the flesh is weak."

Twice he had told them to watch and pray. They were

ashamed. They determined this time, as he again went off alone, that they would stay awake. But, seeing him once more in that agony of spirit, once more wet with blood and sweat, they once more closed their eyes — and once more slept.

Again Jesus asked his Father to remove the chalice. Again he bent his will. This time he assumed the sins of that day and that night, including the sins of Judas and Caiphas and all the other children of disobedience and pride.

He woke the three the second time and left them more ashamed than before. He left them the third time, to assume the sins men would commit until earth's final hour.

This was the most dreadful agony of all; for the years, "the Christian years," were the bloodiest of all. They were the years of persecutions, of annihilating wars, of mass murder, of gas chambers and concentration camps and ruthless dictators and deliberately planned frightfulness and terror. They were the years of pirates, of slave traders, of exploiters — of men who carved empires for themselves out of the bones of the humble and the helpless and the poor, the least of Jesus' brethren; of men who fattened on the blood and the sweat of their victims; of men who walked to comfort on the stairway of their brothers' bodies. They were the years when men made gods of their own intellects; they were the years of religious heresies and hatreds; they were the years of a growing disbelief in God and an ever increasing contempt of love and mercy.

Voices strengthened him in this ordeal, as the angel had done when Jesus first called upon his Father — the voices of men and women who would not be born for hundreds of years. They knew he was still in the garden, and always would be — since he had foreseen all the days that were to be. They could say, "Jesus mercy!" and he would hear them, though he was thousands of years and thousands of miles away. They could say, "Lord, have pity on me, a sinner" and he would be heartened.

Three saints close to him in time and space were sound asleep; other saints would attend him, watching and praying, through the centuries. And some would suffer with him.

When he returned to his sleepyheads the last time, he showed no sign of his ordeal. He had drunk the chalice to the last drop. He was ready to lift the next chalice to his lips. He was in such spirits he could even try a tender joke. "Sleep on now," he said, shaking his friends vigorously awake. "Take your rest!"

They did not laugh. Nor did Jesus. For a rabble of men was making its slow way up the hillside toward the garden, lanterns and torches burning, angry voices calling and cursing.

"The hour has come," Jesus said. "The Son of man is betrayed. Rise now and let us go."

He went forward quickly, facing the mob his enemies had sent to seize him.

CHAPTER XXVIII

Judas smiled as he approached, as though he were bringing these ruffians to a gay party, "Hail, Rabbi," he said, and moved to kiss Jesus on the cheek.

"Friend," Jesus said, "would you betray the Son of man with a kiss?"

Some of the soldiers and priests who had followed Judas edged forward then, intending to arrest their Prisoner. But Jesus looked at them, and they stood where they were — as if they had been paralyzed. "Whom do you seek?" Jesus asked.

"Jesus of Nazareth," one managed to say.

"I am he," Jesus said. There was such power and majesty in him at that moment that the men who had come into the garden with clubs and swords drew back from him and fell on their faces at his feet.

Judas found himself lying on the earth with the priests and soldiers. He kept his eyes tightly shut. He knew now that Jesus was truly the Son of God. He was letting all men see his divinity. He was permitting them to feel it. He was God, and they were less than worms — yet they had dared to move against him. Judas, for the first time, realized the enormity of his crime. "But he'll get away," he told himself. "He'll just walk through them now as though they weren't there. And then — " But he couldn't think of what might happen then. It was too terrible to consider.

"Whom do you seek?" Jesus asked again.

And again a voice just managed to pronounce his name. "Jesus of Nazareth."

"I have told you I am he," Jesus said. "If you want me, let these others go!" Something in his voice gave them the clue that he was only a man again, an ordinary man!

The Word, who was made flesh for men, now must suffer and die in the flesh for men. God could not suffer. God could not die. Jesus was both God and Man; but from that moment on, in the divine mystery of the Redemption, his humanity must increase and his divinity decrease. He had revealed his Godhead to these men so that his followers might escape. Now they must see him only as a man.

The priests and soldiers rose up warily, fumbling for the clubs and the swords and the lanterns they had dropped, relighting the torches that had been extinguished and fouled when they fell to the sandy earth. They came forward slowly, still not believing that the majestic lion who had so badly frightened them had actually turned into docile lamb. It was plain they meant to treat Jesus roughly. It was too much for Peter. He snatched his sword out of its scabbard and struck at the nearest man, cutting off the fellow's ear.

"Put up your weapon," Jesus commanded him. "Those who take the sword will perish by the sword." Jesus was not such a tame lamb, after all, the leaders thought. They hesitated, watching him touch the wound where the ear had been. They saw an ear there. It could not have been the one he had. They had seen that fall, with a gush of blood. Some soldier was probably standing on it now. This was a new ear!

"You have come out with swords and clubs as against a robber," Christ said, gently reproaching them for bringing such an army, and making such a tumult. "I was daily teaching in the Temple. You could have taken me there. But you did not lay a hand on me. . . . But then, this is your hour, and that of the power of darkness."

Some of the men listened respectfully. Others heard not a single word, for they were clustered about the man with the new ear. His name was Malchus. He was a servant — a slave — of the high priest.

"Can you hear?" a soldier asked him.

"I can hear you," Malchus said.

"Now you'll join the Nazarenes," a priest taunted him, "if there are any left when this one dies."

"A Nazarene," one of the other slaves cried. "Malchus is a Nazarene! Wait until the high priest gets the news."

Malchus made a quick step toward his fellow slave and knocked him down with a vicious backhand slap.

Two soldiers gripped Jesus by the shoulders, as though Malchus had given a signal. Another bound the Lord's wrists behind him. Officers shouted orders. Men stirred into action. The Apostles took advantage of the confusion and the darkness and scurried away. But Peter and John kept as close to Jesus as they thought prudent.

Lucifer followed them a little way, then went back to speak to Judas, who lay where he had fallen.

"Congratulations, friends," Lucifer whispered. "Having a nice time being sorry for yourself? That's good. That's very good. I am always happy when anyone pities himself. Do you think your Master pities you? Do you think he would forgive you? You know better. Why don't you go buy a halter with that silver? And why don't you hang yourself? Do it now. And let this be a lesson to you — never trust the devil."

John and Peter followed the noisy procession to the top of the hill of Sion, exchanging only a few words.

"Where's Thomas?" John asked — not expecting any sort of answer. "He wanted to die with him."

"Where's your brother James?" Peter asked in return. "Where are all the others? I'll tell you where they are. They're hiding. They're frightened."

John remembered the time he and his brother James wanted to call down fire from heaven on a Samaritan city that would not let Jesus pass through it on the way to Jerusalem. Jesus had rebuked them for that. Yet John wished now, aloud, that fire would come down to consume all the soldiers and priests in their exultation — and that it would spread to Annas and Caiphas, and all the others who thirsted for the Master's blood.

"He said he could get twelve legions of angels or more," Peter reminded him. "Where are they? Where are they taking him?"

"We must be near the home of Annas, Caiphas' father-in-law," John said. "He is the real high priest. He is the one who runs the Temple, and gets the most money from it. He has hated Jesus ever since the Lord drove the money changers away and called them thieves. They're bringing him to Annas first, so the old mummy can gloat. He does look like a mummy, even with that dirty gray beard!"

The two found an opportunity, when the soldiers and the slaves had gone, to enter a courtyard from which they could see into the house. John, to Peter's surprise, seemed to know all the servants. Nobody tried to hinder them. Nobody questioned them. John explained that he was once his father's agent in Jerusalem. He had delivered many kegs of fish to the house of Caiphas, and to the houses of many other rich men.

They could see Jesus standing tall and straight, his arms bound behind him, looking at Annas with a calm dignity that seemed to infuriate the old man. And John, whose ears were keen, heard some of the conversation.

"What are they saying?" Peter whispered.

"Annas is trying to lure Jesus into talking about us and his other disciples," John told him. I didn't hear everything he said, but I think he wants it to appear that Jesus has been raising an army to threaten Rome. He wants him to say something about his teachings. Maybe he hopes to make him talk about the tribute to Caesar or something equally dangerous."

"And what does Jesus say?" Peter asked.

"Jesus says he has already told his opinions to the world. He has spoken publicly, never in private. If Annas really wants to know what he has said, let him ask those who heard. And Annas — "

John didn't finish what he had been about to say, for the man Malchus had run toward Jesus, shouting, "Is that a way to answer the high priest?" And before anybody could stop him — though nobody tried to — he had lashed out with the back of his hand and brought blood trickling from the corner of Jesus' mouth!

Instinctively Peter's hand went to his sword.

"Listen," John said, "Jesus is speaking."

This time Peter heard the voice. It was calm, gentle, reasonable, without a trace of indignation in it. Peter shoved his partly unsheathed blade back into its scabbard. "If I have spoken evil," Jesus said to Malchus, "give testimony of the evil. But if I have not spoken evil, why did you strike me?"

"Look," John said. "Malchus is overwhelmed. The Lord's words cut deeper than your sword. Annas is overwhelmed too. Jesus is too much for him. He is going to send him to Caiphas."

Peter seemed bewildered. "But why?" he asked. "But why? Why did Malchus strike him? How could he have done such a thing, after Jesus worked a miracle for him?"

"Some men will do more than that," John said, "to get a nod from the lord and master. Malchus wanted to show Annas he had no sympathy for Jesus, in spite of what had happened. Now perhaps he is sorry. Let's go. I know a short cut."

They were sitting in the first courtyard of Caiphas' palace when Jesus was brought in. Again they had had no trouble. The maid at the door had smiled at John and let him in without any question. She looked inquiringly at Peter, but as he was with John she let him pass. Yet after she had thought a little while, she went to look for him. He was standing with John before the fire in the courtyard. He had not felt the cold of the night until now. Now it had penetrated into him. He was as close to the flames as he could get, and he was slapping himself on the shoulders.

"You are one of the Nazarene's followers, aren't you?" the girl asked. Peter looked at her with dull eyes and wished she would go away. She didn't like that. "Certainly you were," she said in a louder voice. She spoke to the others standing about the fire, slaves, guards, servants. "He was with Jesus," she said.

"No," Peter said, shaking his head. "I don't know the Man. I don't know what you're talking about."

The girl went away, but she had not been convinced.

Without attracting too much attention, Peter and John were able to pass through the open door into the hall reserved for the meeting of the Sanhedrin. The members of that august body had been notified hours before. They had waited long before Jesus was brought in to them. They had already condemned him, agreeing with Caiphas that it was expedient he should die for the people. They had to "try" him — for the sake of appearances — even though they broke all their own rules and laws in doing so. It was a long, tedious, exhausting procedure. Witness after witness was called. Witness after witness lied. Peter and John knew they lied. So did all the members of the Sanhedrin. And every new witness contradicted all the others. They had been coached, it was evident, but either they had forgotten their lines or they had been coached by too many priests.

Every so often the two Apostles stepped outside and went back to the fire. There, for the second time, Peter was accosted by suspicious servants. This time a man and a woman accused him. For the second time Peter denied his Lord, this time vehemently, using a salty oath such as he had often used when he fished in the Sea of Galilee. He was still sputtering when he went back into the hall with John.

Caiphas had tired of the foolish witnesses. Now he seemed determined to end the trial, and in his own way, illegal though it might be. He stood on his tiptoes in front of Jesus, lifting both hands high above his head. And he cried out, in a voice that was shrill with malice: "I adjure you, by the living God, tell me: are you the Christ, the Son of God?"

Jesus was standing as he had stood before Annas. Serene, unruffled, the only sane man in the hall. "You have said it," he answered. "I am he. And I tell you that some day you will see the Son of man sitting on the right hand of the power of God, and coming in the clouds of heaven!"

Caiphas knew the Scripture. He knew that Jesus was saying, "Yes, I am God. I have the power of God. And some day you will see me when I come to judge the world!" Everybody else there knew the Scripture, except perhaps Peter and John. And they were seized with a great fright — and also with an intemperate anger.

"You have heard him," Caiphas screamed. "He has blasphemed."

He tore his garments into rags. Ordinarily when a high priest accused anyone of blasphemy he rent his robes — but in a way that didn't hurt them. There was a place where a few threads could be ripped away. That would pass for a ritual rending. And it would save repairs or the cost of new robes. This time Caiphas didn't think of the expense. He had to rip his clothes to appease his emotions.

"What further need of witnesses have we?" he demanded. "You all heard the blasphemy. What do you think?"

The masters of Israel, as one man, dutifully answered: "He is guilty. He should be put to death." But they were not content at thus showing their hatred. They rushed at Jesus more fiercely than the soldiers had when they seized him in the garden. They spat in his face. They pulled his hair and his beard. They struck him with their fists, and slapped him with their open hands. They kicked him.

That wasn't enough. They must show their terrible scorn. They blindfolded him. And as they struck, they cried out, "Who was it struck you, Lord? . . . Tell us who hit you then, you Christ who will come to judge us. . . . Prophesy to us, Son of God, who was it blacked your eye?"

"Let's get out of here," John whispered to Peter. "These are not priests. They are not even men." Angry tears glistened in his eyes.

The two slipped out of the hall unobserved and made their way back, through the shadows, toward the clean and welcoming flames.

"Here is the Galilean," a man shouted. "Here is the Nazarene."

"Me?" Peter said. "Me a Galilean?"

"Your accent gives you away," his accuser said. "Of course you are a Nazarene. Didn't I see you in the garden with your Master?"

"I tell you," Peter said, shouting as loudly as the other, "I do not know the Man."

Again he cursed and swore. And while he was still protesting that he did not know Jesus, he looked up and saw Jesus being hustled past him by two guards. Jesus looked at Peter.

Somewhere a cock crowed.

Peter rushed away, blinded with tears.

John lingered in the courtyard until he saw the guards lower Jesus, on a stout rope, through a round hole in the floor near the fireplace. There was a prison at the bottom of that hole, an iron cage erected in a natural cave. Jesus would be kept there, John knew, until Caiphas was ready to hold the second trial. His arms and legs would be thrust through the bars, and fettered. And the guards would have their way with him, now that their masters had satisfied their fury.

He said good-night to his friends in the courtyard, and set out for the house in Bethany where Martha and Mary had expected to welcome Mary, the mother of Jesus.

He must tell them all that had happened. But perhaps the Lord's Mother already knew. She knew many things, the lovely gracious lady, that no man or woman had ever told her. John hoped she knew. And he hoped she would not ask: "Where was Philip, where was Thomas, where was your brother James?" He hoped she would not ask about Peter.

CHAPTER XXIX

Lucifer attended the second trial held by Caiphas shortly before dawn. It was a repetition of the first. Jesus emerged a great man, an innocent man, a kingly man. His accusers looked the murderers they were. Jesus had made them conscious of their sins, the devil noticed, and ashamed of them. They were even aware of the necessity of punishment for sin. But they were not big enough to punish themselves. They were punishing their Victim instead. Lucifer was bored, yet he was amazed too. There wasn't one soul there worth dying for, he felt; yet this Man, this great Prophet, thought otherwise.

They brought Jesus to Herod after they had taken him before Pilate. He made an ass of Herod by not saying a single word to him; just as he had made fools of Annas and Caiphas by simply being himself. Lucifer, in spite of himself, could not help admiring Jesus as he was brought back from Herod to Pilate, shackled hand and foot. He was not a citizen who had gone through civilized courts of law. He looked more like a man ambushed by savage tribesmen. He had been shamefully treated; yet there was no anger in him, no indignation, no scorn.

He probably was not what he claimed to be, since he had a human father and mother. Yet he was all man. He was a greater man than ever. The pious and righteous members of the

Sanhedrin had made a hero and a martyr of him. Now they were going to kill him "for the people." That wasn't going to kill his ideas. On the contrary. His dying "for the people" would keep him alive for generations!

Lucifer was frightened by his esteem for Jesus; yet he was enraged by the failure of Annas and Caiphas to degrade him. He realized he was a fool to trust such proud hypocrites. Could he trust Pilate, a man who hated the high priests, a man who had no belief at all in the God of Israel?

Lucifer had been present when Jesus was led, with a chain around his neck, to the justice of Pontius Pilate. The neck chain told Pilate that Jesus had been condemned to death by the Jews, and that they wanted him to crucify the man.

Pilate had asked, "Are you the king of the Jews?" He had been urbane, polite, even respectful, in sharp contrast to the conduct of the high priests. "You have said it," Jesus had answered solemnly. "For this was I born; for this have I come into the world, that I should give testimony to the truth." And he had told Pilate that His kingdom was not of this world.

Pilate had asked, "What is truth?" and had hurried out to the chief priests and lawyers without waiting for an answer. The masters of Israel remained outside the praetorium. To enter it, they believed, would defile them. That would keep them from celebrating the Passover.

Because of this situation, Pilate had had to go in and out, as often as the needle of a busy seamstress.

He seemed glad to learn that Jesus was a Nazarene. Herod, tetrarch of Galilee was in Jerusalem. Pilate had thought he could dispose of the case and rid himself of all responsibility for the death of this innocent Man by sending Him to Herod for judgment. There was more justice, more charity, and more compassion in this Roman heathen, the devil thought, than in the priests of the one true God. Yet Pilate would let someone else do the dirty work. The man could be handled when the time came to handle him.

Lucifer had been bored by Herod also. That obese sot, who once had believed Jesus to be the ghost or the reincarnation of John the Baptist, was delighted when Pilate referred Jesus to him. He had organized a party and invited as many guests as his palace would hold. He meant to have an entertainment rather than a trial. He wanted to make Jesus do some of his tricks.

Jesus would not even acknowledge Herod was alive. He was the real king in that palace. Herod knew it. Everybody knew it. Herod, trying to make a fool of him, put a fool's robe on him. The Man still looked like the only king there, Herod the only fool. So Herod had sent Jesus back to Pilate, and had returned to his wine.

Pilate, Lucifer saw, was doing all he could to save Jesus from his enemies. So was Pilate's wife. She had had a dream that troubled her, and had asked her husband to have nothing to do with "this just man." Pilate bade a soldier to remove the fool's robe from Jesus and unshackle his legs. Then he went outside to bargain with the crowd of accusers. It was the custom for the governor to release a prisoner during this great feast. He would give them their choice: Jesus, who was called the Christ, or Barabbas, a robber and a killer.

Lucifer lost most of his worry. These killers would naturally choose to free the killer — and to kill Jesus. But he wasn't taking any chances. Therefore he whispered in several hundred ears. And several hundred angry and excited men shouted the name, "Barabbas!"

"Then what shall I do with Jesus?" Pilate asked.

Lucifer whispered the words, and his friends repeated them: "Crucify him!"

Pilate hushed them, finally. "I will release Barrabbas," he

said. "But I have found no guilt in Jesus, nothing deserving of death. I will scourge him and release him."

He hurried inside before they could cry out their disappointment and their fury. He was glad to get away from them, even if it were only for a few moments. Lucifer took the occasion to whisper instructions to Caiphas: "Restrain your mob for a little while. What can you lose? Pilate thinks you will relent when you see him, his back cut into bloody rags by the Roman whips. He doesn't know you, does he? Let Jesus be scourged now. You can crucify him later. Try to be patient, however difficult you find it. Forget your charge of blasphemy. He could blaspheme against your God a hundred times and it wouldn't matter to Pilate. But if you can show he blasphemed against Caesar, you have Pilate clutched in your hot greedy fist. And you can squeeze him until he gives you what you want."

The demon went into the courtyard with Jesus and his guards. He watched the men strip the Prisoner, fasten him to a pillar, and prepare to flog him. There were two lictors, two husky soldiers, inspecting their favorite whips. The younger man — he was in his middle twenties, Lucifer saw — would strike the first blows. When he began to tire, the older man — who looked to be forty or more — would take his place. Lucifer approved of the lictors. They looked as inhuman as bull apes — and as intelligent. He could see they were fond of their weapons and would take pride in stripping a man of his flesh without killing him in the process.

And Lucifer fully approved of the whips. They were beautiful long-tongued cats. The tips of their tongues were equipped with pretty teeth that would scratch and gouge and rip and rend.

The cats sang as they swished through the air. Lucifer knew hellish ecstacy, listening to them, and to the sound their leather tongues made in smacking the bare flesh of the Victim.

Yet his worry and his fear and his fury mounted as the whips
rose and swished and fell, and no sound came from Jesus. Lucifer knew that Jesus must be suffering as no other man had suffered — and he had known every child who lived to be a man.
Jesus was the Perfect Man, physically, mentally, spiritually;
hence he was far more sensitive to pain, or to anything that might
impair the perfection of his body, than any other man could be.
He had, undoubtedly, suffered more, in last night's beatings, than
any man in history, including that holy man, Job. Now as the
tongues of the cats licked at him, he was blazing with pain and
simmering in agony of soul. Still he remained silent, meek, regal!
And there was always that tender pity in his eyes.

Lucifer thought he was trying to make a fool of him too. Did
he rate the lord of hell with such cackling geese as Annas and
Caiphas! Lucifer would show him his mistake. He would break
Jesus, make him whimper, make him beg, make him grovel.

"If you were actually the Son of God," he said to Jesus, "you
would save yourself needless pain. You would bid these two
dumb brutes to cease, and they would do it. We met in the
desert. You remember. You were rude to me. You were younger
then, and at the beginning of your power. I hold no malice,
because I understand. Now give up your absurd claim to my
throne, and I will save you. I am the king of sinners. Not you.
I share my throne with no one. I do not intend to hinder you,
if you do not hinder me. Give me your word, and all will be
well. You will go your way, I mine."

Jesus, reading his thoughts, ignored him.

"Pilate ordered only thirty lashes for you." Lucifer was never
averse to telling a lie. "You have had thirty already. The young
man cannot count. The older one can count up to ten, but he
forgets the count and has to start all over again."

Lucifer smoldered, but he no longer enjoyed the dance of the
leather tongues on the bleeding back. He was no longer amused

by seeing Jesus' blood trickle down his sides. He was worried now that Jesus would die before he could be affixed to the cross of shame. He was an extremely strong man. Malchus, who had knocked down a companion with a blow of his open hand, had failed to sway Jesus even slightly. Yet even the strongest of men could be beaten to death by those whips.

Lucifer's suffering and frustration and fear increased. Those whips were beating him, he realized, even as they beat his enemy. It was he who weakened, he who broke.

"You think you'll reach the rock in those brutes, and they will gush forth a stream of tears! You think you are better than Moses! I saw you look at Peter and at Malchus. You brought water out of those hard rocks. But those who beat you now are not men. There is no rock in them, only clay. If you be the Son of God, stop them. Stop them now."

Jesus was breathing hard. But he said no word.

Lucifer used his devilish power in sheer self-defense. He caused the men to stop. "Now, O mighty King," Lucifer said, "I've given you a respite. A short one. I once offered you a crown. You spurned it. Now I give you another, woven especially for you."

The soldiers had fun with Jesus. He was a king, was he? Where was his scarlet robe? Where was his scepter? Where was his crown? Where were his loyal friends? Where were his slaves?

They rushed about the courtyard, making a costume for him. They put a soldier's red cloak around his shoulders. They put a reed in his hand. They plaited a crown of thorns and jammed it down on his head. It looked like a helmet, but it pleased the soldiers to think of it as a royal crown. They bowed low to him and spat on him. They praised and pummeled him.

Lucifer laughed, with a laugh he used in hell, as another soldier struck Jesus with a reed.

"That reed is a shoddy symbol, I admit," he said. "A reed is not the scepter for you, though it has its purposes. It made the man who struck you feel big. It made you look weak — and cheap! A king who could be lashed with a reed! I'll have a real scepter ready for you — after we return to your jellyfish champion, Pilate."

He accompanied Jesus back to the praetorium. He stood with him and with Pilate, when the governor showed him to the people.

"I bring him out to you," Pilate cried, "that you may know I find no guilt in him. Behold the Man!"

"Crucify him," hundreds of voices shouted. "Crucify him!"

Pilate hesitated. He questioned Jesus. Jesus did not answer. Pilate was annoyed. "Why don't you speak up?" he said. "Don't you know I have the power to crucify you or to release you?"

"He has already half-killed you," Lucifer said, "and he will not release you — unless you make a bargain with me."

Jesus spoke to Pilate: "You would have no power over me if it were not given you from above. Therefore, he who betrayed me to you has the greater sin."

What Pilate started to say was lost in the fury of sound made by the mob. One voice came clearly out of the tumult: "If you release that Man, you are no friend of Caesar's."

Pilate washed his hands in front of the hostile crowd.

"I am innocent of the blood of this just Man," he shouted.

They shouted back: "His blood be on us and on our children."

Pilate tried one last trick. "Behold your King," he said, gesturing. "Shall I crucify your King?" The effort failed dismally. "We have no king but Caesar," they yelled. "Away with this Man. Crucify him!"

Pilate surrendered. He was a friend of Caesar's.

Lucifer wondered why he didn't feel jubilant. A glance at Jesus told him why. He still didn't know whether Jesus was merely a great and powerful friend of the Most High or whether he was God, and the Son of God.

Could it be possible God was so humble and meek, so willing to die for men — God who had so dreadfully punished sinners in the past? Yes, Lucifer decided, it could be possible. He was disturbed again. But no! It was impossible. God could not love sinners as much as this Man, Jesus, seemed to love them.

Lucifer was himself again.

"Crucify him," he cried. "Crucify him. Aye. His blood be on your heads!"

CHAPTER XXX

Lucifer approved of the cross Caiphas had selected. It was heavier than any tree trunk Jesus had carried when he was a carpenter. Yet it was not too heavy. Oh, it would give him trouble in his weakened condition. But the soldiers would help him, even with the flats of their swords.

Lucifer loved the splinters in it. The whips had gnawed both of Jesus' shoulders, but there was enough flesh left for the splinters.

"Behold your throne, O King," Lucifer said to Jesus, watching the little group of slaves who dragged it forward. It was heavy for them. Would it be too heavy for Jesus? He began to doubt again. Always his moments of triumph were marred with doubt or worry or fear; or they were ruined by some stupid human act or by some action from above. He could never fully enjoy his victories.

"Caiphas chose it with care," he said. "A great cross for a great enemy. A royal deathbed for a king — the King of Jews. Reign on it forever, O conquering Nazarene! Forever and forever and a day!"

He was embarrassed, later, when he remembered that last remark. "Embarrassed," is a mild word. A very mild word. He was further embarrassed when he learned how the cruel and ugly crown he had given Jesus would be treasured by the world; and how revered the cross would be.

The devil, always in a feverish hurry, chided Caiphas for the delay. "The sooner we go, the sooner he dies," he reminded the high priest. "He must die before the Sabbath starts. He claims to be the Lord of the Sabbath; but you are the Sabbath's slave. You will be defiled if he lives to greet its coming."

Thus, ironically, the devil sent a great crowd walking toward the first Holy Mass, in the first pilgrimage of the Christian era, the first solemn procession of the new Church, the first "Stations of the Cross."

He would have said more, but a light flashed into his conciousness and confused and frightened him. He leaped into a shelter in back of the high priest's eyes, so he could see without being dazzled. It was Mary, the mother of Jesus, who stood there, shining with such splendor. Why had she come? To upset his plans? She had been in Galilee. Why had she come to Jerusalem? To fight him? Jesus had said he could ask for legions of angels. How many legions was this woman worth?

Rage seized him, driving out fear. She was "terrible as an army set in battle array," but Lucifer had scattered many armies. She had come to help her Son? She would fail! Nothing would prevent this crucifixion. Nothing in heaven, on earth, or in hell.

The Roman herald was blowing his trumpet and calling out the name of the prisoners and their crimes. "Jesus of Nazareth, King of the Jews." Caiphas jumped up and down in anger and indignation. The herald was holding up a wooden sign, which was to be tacked to the cross. Caiphas read the words, written in three languages. "Jesus of Nazareth, King of the Jews." He had asked Pilate to make it read, "He said he was the King of the Jews"; but Pilate had walked away from him as though he were a leprous beggar, saying, "What I have written, I have written."

Lucifer felt uncomfortable, looking out of the eyes of the priest. He wished Caiphas would relax so that a harassed and worried devil could have time to think about that light. Nobody around Mary seemed to have noticed anything unusual. Nobody seemed to know she emitted rays of glory. Lucifer alone had seen that. God had wanted him to see it. Why? What frightful strategy had she prepared against him?

Mary had walked from Bethany with Mary Magdalen, with her niece, Salome, and with Salome's mother, Mary Alpheus — or as some people called her, Mary Cleophas. Mary Alpheus, her sister-in-law, and Salome, had accompanied her from Capharnaum.

The women, led by John, had started early in the morning. They had walked slowly, weeping a little, talking a little, trying now and then to laugh — though they did not feel like laughing. Only the mother of Jesus seemed her usual self. John could see that her heart was broken yet she did not act as if it were.

She stopped now and then to admire a tree or to watch a bird in flight or to pick a wild flower and inhale the scent the Lord God had given it or to look at the white clouds in the blue-gray sky or to enjoy the pattern of light and shade some rude wall boasted or to stand and praise God for the beauty of his Temple shining with gold beneath the golden sun.

"Even from this distance," she said to John, "I can hear the bleating of the sacrificial lambs."

John choked with the emotion she aroused in him. Mary Magdalen sobbed. Mary Alpheus said, "Now, now, let's not think of such things; I don't think anything terrible will happen; it would be too awful."

The Virgin Mother smiled at her sadly, but made no comment.

"Joseph and I went through this street," she told John, with some little excitement and some hint of recaptured joy, "when we were going to Bethlehem. Joseph was worried because he could find no inn, nor any friend who would let us have a room."

At another stop she said, "I rested here, the day we found him in the Temple. I couldn't walk any more, or I thought I couldn't. Joseph made me sit down. He held my hand and gave me strength. Power went out from him, sometimes — even as it goes out from Jesus. Not the same power. But enough for me. Joseph gave me the courage and the strength I needed."

Jerusalem was filled with memories, but she could not share them all, even with those she so loved.

John had his memories too; but he did not think of sharing them with anyone.

Unlike Lucifer he saw no unusual light shining around Mary. She was, to him, a simple country woman, middle-aged, dressed in red and brown garments she had probably made at home. She was the kind of woman people loved to help, whom everybody obeyed cheerfully and without asking why. She was the sort of woman everybody sought when in trouble or need. She was a woman beautiful beyond all telling; yet filled with such sorrow, and such compassion, that, at first, one didn't realize that she was beautiful. John wondered how a woman so exquisitely lovely could also be so exquisitely humble. And he wondered at the depths of her sorrows and the heights of her serenity.

There was dust on her hands and her feet, on her cheeks, on the bridge of her nose, and beneath her glorious eyes. There was dust on her clothing and on the veil that covered her hair. Yet she looked as immaculate and fresh and fragrant as the half-dozen lilies of the valley she had found on the way from Bethany, and which she had kissed and given to the other Marys and to her pet, Salome.

They had no trouble penetrating the crowds when they neared the praetorium. Men and women turned to look at Mary, and made way for her as though she were a queen. Thus they arrived in time to see the cross placed on Jesus' shoulder and to see him stagger beneath its weight and fall to the earth.

They heard the angry cries that rose from the mob. The people thought he was trying to cheat them, to die before he reached the Hill of the Skull. They cursed him. They pelted him with stones and clumps of earth and handfuls of sand and dust and gravel and manure. John expected Mary would rush forward and help her Son to rise, that she would throw her arms around him, that she would make some sort of scene. But she remained unruffled, though tears came to her eyes. "He has no one to help him," she said softly.

Immediately, as though he had heard her, the centurion laid hold of an African — a farmer, evidently — and forced him to help Jesus with the cross. The man protested vehemently: "I am not a Jew. I am Simon of Cyrene. You cannot do this to me!" The centurion stared at him. "Can't I?" he asked.

Simon submitted with bad grace. He bent to lift the heavy cross. He could not raise it an inch. Jesus, struggling up, put a hand on the upright beam. Simon lifted it without any trouble. His eyes opened wide with wonder. "I guess you can," he said to the centurion.

Jesus saw his mother and the little group around her. He shook the dust from himself and rose to his full height.

The last time Mary had seen her Son he was going away from her with his Apostles. Birds had been singing all around her. She had heard the music of the surf on the shores of the Sea of Galilee. She had seen the sun shining on the dust of the road. And she had prayed to see him at least once again if it were God's will.

God had heard her prayers. Here he was again. Alone. All his Apostles had fled — save one. He had been beaten. She hardly recognized his face. He was covered with blood and sweat and dirt. There was a hideous helmet of thorns pressed down on his matted hair, and there were welts and stripes and wounds on his arms and legs and shoulders. He was her Son; and her heart indeed ached for him, even more than John suspected, but he was also her God. And one who looks at God has ventured into heaven.

Heaven looked at heaven once more. Again it saw the glory and the riches and the might of the Promised Land of God, and the barrenness and misery of the earth. This time it also saw the Promised Land unloading its treasures, emptying itself of its graces, even as the skies empty themselves of rain and sleet and hail and snow.

"How can you," Mary Magdalen asked, on the verge of hysteria, "how can you bear so terrible a sight and be so calm, so passive, so — so forgiving?"

"If my Son were going away to suffer and die for this Israel of ours," the virgin mother said, "you would weep, even as you weep now; yet you would glory in his courage, his patriotism, his unselfishness, the love he bears for every one of us. You would be more than proud he loved you and yours."

"He goes to die for sinners like me," the Magdalen said, "That's why I cannot help weeping."

"Weep for sinners," Mary said. "Weep for Judas."

"Judas hanged himself," Salome said. "I heard it a little while ago. Two women near me were talking about him. He threw the money on the Temple floor and went out and killed himself."

"Pray for him," Mary said. "And don't think he died in black despair and went to hell. For all we know, he may have asked for mercy before he died. If so, he is not damned. Would you see how infinite is God's mercy? Look at Jesus there before you, carrying his cross!"

Mary Alpheus came close to the virgin mother. "I did not dream it would be so awful, so more than awful."

CHAPTER XXXI

Until this moment John had known as much horror as grief. He had made wild plans for rescuing his Lord. He had even imagined dying with him, in a grand fight that took a dozen enemies with him into the life beyond. He had discarded all these dreams, realizing Jesus would never approve of them. He had also known an intense hatred and a desire for revenge — or for the vengeance of God.

Now he began to share something of Mary's compassion, and a fraction of her exaltation. He was actually taking part in a march of triumph, he told himself, the greatest triumph the world would ever know, the victory of Love and Mercy over all the enemies of man. He felt, as he had at the Transfiguration, that it was good to be here, a witness. He didn't know why he had been so blessed. He was the youngest and the least of all the Apostles; yet the only one privileged to walk with the mother of Jesus in her profoundest sorrow — to be with her when she was most in need of him. He could both mourn and rejoice with her in the victorious defeat and the conquering death of her Son. He, John! It was a miracle of God's grace!

He looked again and again at his Lord, though sometimes tears blinded him. Jesus had more authority over him now than at any other time, even on that mountaintop when he had revealed his glory. Words the Lord had said, and to which John had paid scant attention, were now commands to be implicitly obeyed.

Peter had asked how many times he should forgive his brother. Seven times? That was a figure of speech that meant not just seven times, but a great many. "Not seven times," Jesus had said, "but seventy times seven." That meant "forgive him with all your heart, without any limits, without any reservations."

Therefore, John decided, he would forgive all those who hated Jesus, who kept spitting at him, who kept cursing him and jeering at him, who kept urging him to quit loitering and hurry, so they might see him lifted up against the sky. John would forgive them seventy times seven. Could he do that? Mary would help him. She had, he knew, already forgiven them. The way she looked upon them one would think they were her children too, and that she was more sorry for them than she was for Jesus.

For the first time he noticed that Mary's eyes were curiously like those of her Son. And for the first time he realized she had a way of reading minds and hearts — even as Jesus had. For she said to him: "Yes, forgive them. And pray for them. Whatsoever you do for the least of these, his brethren, you do for him."

John prayed for them and remembered another thing Jesus had commanded: "Love your enemies; do good to them who hate you." So he would love these Pharisees and Sadducees and Scribes, these murderous masters of Israel. He would do it in spite of himself. It was unnatural. It was definitely unnatural. But one who followed Jesus must live not a natural life, but a supernatural one. He must control his rebellious nature. He must unite himself to God, as closely as he could. God loved everybody. Even Caiphas! John must love Caiphas too!

Love! That was the whole of the Master's life. Love! For love he had lived and healed and taught and preached. For love he had suffered injuries and slights and spittle and thorns and stripes. For love he had endured an agony of soul that pumped blood out of his face like sweat. For love he had undergone intolerable loneliness, rejection by his nearest and dearest friends, the most degrading shame — even the defilement of man's sins! For love he would suffer physical agony and death. And through love he would conquer the bitter hateful world!

Indeed this was a march of triumph.

He began to notice other things than the drama on the road ahead. He began to see some of the things Mary saw — things that sang to her of God. Palm trees dripping dates; songbirds showing gaudy colors; stones shining in the heavy dust; dust glinting as it rose and spiraled to the somber sky; the grace and beauty of the centurion's horse; the wild flowers that wandered through the city.

He was looking at the bloody footprints his Lord had made in the dust and the stones of the street, and trying not to see them, when Salome slipped by him and darted through the mocking priests and the menacing soldiers. She ran straight to Jesus. John saw a soldier move toward her, scowling; saw him wave his sword. He took a step toward the soldier; but Mary restrained him with a touch and a wan sad smile.

John hung his head in shame. He had forgotten about forgiveness and love. So soon! So impossibly soon! He had thought only of rescuing Jesus' little cousin. The knowledge that he might be hacked to pieces before he could save her, or that he might be spitted on a lance, had occurred to him; but he had dismissed it. Why? Because his anger and his hate had been stronger than his fear. He almost blushed with embarrassment and self-contempt. Yet he tried to justify himself.

"Must one see innocence imperiled and do nothing?" he asked.

"Sometimes," Mary answered, "one may go to the rescue, even at a sacrifice. But never in anger, never with any lessening of

love. And sometimes one must indeed see Innocence imperiled
and do nothing."

She nodded toward her Son who had fallen the second time.
He lay sprawled, face down, in the filth and gravel and dust
and stones. Soldiers kicked him, pulled at his arms and shoulders,
yanked his blood-starched beard, tried to lift him to his feet with
yells and curses.

The centurion rode his mount into the crowd of fanatic men
and women — and excited little boys — who were trying to reach
the fallen Man so they might help the soldiers beat and kick
new life and strength into him. He swung his sword above them,
making it gleam wickedly in the glaring sunlight. They ran
screaming from him and from his horse's hoofs. The centurion
roared at his men: "How many daring Roman legionaries are
needed to lift one half-dead Jew? Do you think you can raise
him by killing him? Try helping him."

"Jesus has his cross," Mary said, watching her Son get to his
feet and put his shoulder to the wood again. "We have ours.
He must suffer and die. We must watch him suffer and die. We
must stand by his cross and do nothing. We will suffer thus, and
we will die a little. Yet we will rejoice that we may do so; for
thus we fulfill our roles in the redemption."

"Innocence will be crucified," John said. "And we, the guilty,
will stand by without even trying to help him. We will suffer only
shame and the knowledge of our sins. Which is the harder to
bear — pain and death — or guilt and shame?"

Jesus was walking again, with difficulty. John noticed he was
no longer sweating.

The sun had gone behind a mass of dirty gray clouds; and
there was an odd yellow light in the sky. There was a gust of
wind that sent the dust flying and carried the scents and sounds
of Jerusalem to the marchers.

"He must have a rest," Mary said.

Immediately, as if in answer to her prayer, a woman, higher up the ascending street, ran toward the procession, screaming, "Jesus, Jesus, Jesus!" John recognized her. She was the woman taken in adultery and brought to Jesus by the Pharisees that they might entrap and humble him — the woman no man had stoned. Others joined in her passionate race, weeping and wailing, and crying out; "Jesus, Son of David . . . Rabbi . . . Master . . . Holy Son of the Most High . . . Savior of Israel . . . Jesus, the Christ, the Messiah!"

The centurion halted the procession, and faced the women calmly. Some of them screamed insults at him, which he pretended not to hear. Some tried to reach him — unafraid of the lances held in a grim steady line — to claw and scratch him. Jesus stood straight beneath his cross and looked at them. They quieted immediately. He did not see them, John was certain, for one of his eyes had been closed by a blow, and the other was covered with dried blood that had trickled from wounds made by the thorns.

"Daughters of Jerusalem," he said, "weep not for me, but for yourselves and for your children."

John saw his mother in the crowd of women listening to Jesus. Her face was red and swollen. John was touched by the sight. He had never loved her so much in all his life. Yet he could not help comparing her to the woman at his side. His mother had ambitions for him and James. She had even hoped Jesus would put one on a throne by his right side, when he came into his kingdom, and the other on his left. Mary had no ambitions for her Son, though she loved him as no other mother had ever loved a child. She had never tried to make him "important." She had never tried to dissuade him from sacrificing himself for sinners. Now she was helping him make that sacrifice. She was sacrificing herself with him!

He wondered what his mother would say if it were himself, and not Jesus, there on the road, staggering under the weight of the cross. And he wondered what "Old Thunderhead" — God, be good to him — would say.

Something distracted him. A woman's grasp, a cry of wonder and delight. He looked around and saw Salome. She was staring at the cloth that had touched the face of Jesus. Her eyes were shining with such love and happiness John was angered, for a moment. He wanted to shake her. Was this a time for ecstasy? But then, over her shoulder, he saw what the Lord had given her — the imprint of his face, with all his woe and all his love and all his royalty stamped upon it! John almost fell to his knees in veneration — but he heard his mother's voice.

Suddenly he made a decision. "Let's go through this shop," he said, leading Mary out through the press and making sure the others followed. "Otherwise we'll never get through the crowd ahead. This is a short cut." He didn't want to meet his mother. She might be afraid for him, and for James too. She might try to drive him away, out of all danger. She might ask about James. He wondered how Jesus had felt when he met his mother and saw the way she suffered for him.

He hadn't heard everything Jesus had said to the women; but he knew it had something to do with the destruction of Jerusalem, which the Lord had so many times predicted. Women without children would be blessed in those days. They might flee. They would not have any little ones to impede them, to make them helpless. People would be so terrified, and so conscious of their guilt, they would ask the mountains to fall upon them and hide them.

But John had distinctly heard the last words Jesus said to them: "For if in the green wood they do these things, what shall be done in the dry?" He wondered about those words as he led the women through a small store, into a narrow, dark, wretched, stinking, winding street, and out through the genneth gate.

The storekeeper nodded as they passed by, not acknowledging their presence, merely watching to make sure they stole nothing from him.

John thought he knew what Jesus meant. Whatever a man does in the green wood of his life will have some consequence in the dry wood of eternity. And what he fails to do, or neglects to do, or shirks doing, will also have its effects hereafter. Death, he thought, was only a door. It was a door made of dry and weathered wood. It opened on eternal misery or eternal joy. Each man opened his own door and entered into the place assigned him. He opened it with a key he himself had fashioned while the wood was green.

He led the way up a flight of stairs, through another path, onto the Hill of the Skull. He paused, startled at the beauty stretched out before him. The grim rock was covered with patches of moss, and with wild flowers of all kinds and all colors. A beautiful carpet on an ugly altar!

Jesus had fallen again.

The centurion's horse had taken fright at something. Maybe it was the noisy flight of bedraggled crows that went winging by, flying low. Maybe it was the lowering clouds, the darkening sky, the sudden closeness of the air, the signs of a terrible storm gathering in the heavens. Maybe it was the rumble of distant thunder, the queer feel of lightnings overhead, or the slight trembling of the earth.

The officer dismounted and gave the animal to a soldier, who led him away. "Lanterns!" the centurion ordered. "Torches! Let's have some light here. Lots of light. We can't kill men in the dark."

It had become dark as midnight, yet it was scarcely noon. Through a jagged hole in a black sky, John could see a few dull, unwinking stars.

Lanterns were lit here and there and lifted high. Torches flared, stinking, sending up vile columns of black smoke. By these rude lights the soldiers were stripping Jesus.

They were rough. They were hurried. They feared the weather, the seasick earth that rose and fell as though it were water and not rock, the thunder that stayed far out, and the lightnings that would not show themselves. They were clumsy. They tore away parts of Jesus' flesh as they pulled his garments from his lacerated back and sides.

John felt violence in the pit of his stomach when he saw the ragged red, raw flesh of his Lord. He might have given way to his feeling of nausea had not Mary gripped his great right hand and dug her cold hard fingers into it. Her fingers hurt. John was glad they did. The hurt eased the pain in his stomach, and in his mind, and in his heart.

Mary was shaking; and she was talking. He bent closer, not hearing what she said. But it was not to him she talked. "Prince Joseph," she whispered, "Prince Joseph, help me now as you helped me then. I need you. Oh, I need you, Joseph. My dear Joseph. Give me the courage to go on. Give me strength. Keep my will his. Help me, Joseph. Help me! Help me! Help me!"

She did not see the soldiers spread her Son upon the cross and fasten him securely there with heavy spikes. But she could not help hearing the sounds the hammers made on iron and on flesh. She could not help hearing the exultant jeers of the Scribes and Pharisees and their friends. She did not have to see. She knew.

The sword old Simeon had mentioned had been twisted in her heart. She would bear it with patience, with serenity — even with joy. John knew this, somehow, as he gloried in the pain her fingers gave him.

Joseph, her husband, he thought, must have been a very holy man. John prayed to him also.

CHAPTER XXXII

Lucifer, alert in his cramped human quarters, watched the soldiers raise the cross at the edge of the hole prepared for it in the rock. He knew a moment of pure hellish pleasure as they let it drop. For the Man on it was shaken so terribly he seemed actually to dance.

His arms pulled at the nails that fastened them to the crosspiece. His head flashed to right and to left and back to right again. His legs were contorted. His chest and shoulders writhed. His face, even in the poor light of the torches, rippled with spasms of pain. Yet he still was silent.

The woman of the light, the woman terrible as an army set in battle array, had not made the slightest move to save her Son. Nor had that Son tried to save himself. Those two significant facts worried the devil, even now. They sullied his pleasure. Caiphas soiled it too.

The high priest had been congratulating himself on his victory. He had given himself full credit for all the planning, even to putting his enemy to death in the company of two low thieves. Everything had worked perfectly for him. The Sanhedrin would give him honors. He would be the biggest man in Israel. But now he was scanning the fearful skies, as Judas had done, hoping the lightning would spare him. He was trying to convince himself he never had believed Jesus was actually the Son of God. He was trying to excuse himself. He was pleading self-defense. It was either Jesus or himself! He must either follow the religion of a lowborn Carpenter who did miracles on the Holy Sabbath, ate with publicans and sinners, preached arrant nonsense about turning the other cheek, and offered his flesh as meat and his blood as drink — or he must follow the laws of Moses as interpreted and practiced by his people for centuries. Either he or Jesus had to be wrong. It was expedient the one in error should be Jesus.

Of course it was possible, Caiphas was forced to admit, that he had been wrong and Jesus right. Heaven and earth seemed to be appalled at what he had done. But it was too late to undo it. He was thinking of hurrying home; and there was a childish wish forming in his mind that he could lower his dignity enough to let him crawl under a bed and shiver privately with the ague of fright which had attacked him.

Lucifer loved a sinner — as much as a demon can love anything — but he hated a fool. He could no longer abide the priest. He had a better hiding place — the mind of the thief on the nearest cross. He flew to his new refuge even as he thought about it. Both those thieves were old friends. Lucifer liked the big fellow much better than the other. He was easier to handle. That fellow would take the last rites of hell, as administered by Lucifer, and die as a sinner should.

"Don't worry," Lucifer addressed his new host. "It will be over soon. Then, nothing. Nothing at all. No God. No devil. No heaven. No hell. No anything. Meantime, be a man. Yell. Curse. Tell that Prophet hanging next to you what you think of him and his religion. He uses religion as a club, like all the other reformers. He clubs you and controls you. Whatever you do is wrong. Die cursing him. Die cursing God. The storybook God they used to tame and cage you. The God that does not exist. The God who put you here to die."

He would have said more, but he heard Jesus whispering. "Father, forgive them, for they know not what they do."

It was a whisper, yet it beat like thunder on the consciousness of the prince of hell. And it shook the earth more surely than the tremors creeping through the rock.

Lucifer fell to the earth among the soldiers dicing for the seamless garment of the Lord. And he lay prostrate adoring the Most High as every angel must, in heaven or in hell or on the earth.

He had felt the love and the mercy of God as surely as, aeons ago, he had felt the Lord's anger and justice. It had dropped him as suddenly and as deeply into hell. And never had he suffered so terribly as he did now, knowing that Jesus was divine!

One moment he had felt himself gloriously reigning as the king of sinners; the next moment he lay in agony at the foot of the cross, the throne of the real king — the meanest and lowest slave in the kingdom.

Once, he recalled, he had rebelled against the Almighty. He had said, "I shall not serve," and he had led his terrible armies into battle. That had been a proud moment, though he had lost. Now he realized he had served, in spite of himself. God had used him as though he were only a simple creature. God had even taken advantage of his hellish malice to bring about the heavenly purpose. Lucifer knew now that Mary was the virgin promised by the Lord, the woman who would crush the serpent's head. Joseph had been a virgin too. He had married the virgin merely to protect her and the Child. He had fooled Lucifer most shamefully!

It was this marriage that had blinded Lucifer to the truth, that had led him, eventually, to planning this crucifixion — which, he now knew, had really been planned, from all eternity, by the Most High himself! Had Lucifer known Jesus was God, he would — he told himself — have stayed away from him. He

certainly would not have helped the Christ to establish his kingdom on earth. If he could tear Jesus from the cross even now,
he would do it. He knew the despair of Caiphas, but a greater
despair by far. "It is too late!"

Now Jesus would cleanse his kingdom with the water of baptism, and with the blood still gushing from his wounds. (How
could a man even a man who was also God, shed so much blood
and still have life in him?)

And having established his kingdom, Jesus would fortify it
with His sacraments. He would feed his soldiers with his own
flesh and blood, thus strengthening them against all hell, and
making them saints!

But was he, Lucifer, helpless against the Lord? Was his defeat
a rout, a massacre, an annihilation, a divine destruction that
would stay destroyed forever? No, Lucifer vowed. He would
still make relentless war on God, and all the children of God.
As soon as he was able to — as soon as he recovered from the
shock of knowing he had tried to outmaneuver God — he would
return to the attack. But he would never forgive himself for
helping in his own destruction. He would live in perpetual self-
hatred and in undying shame. That was his new punishment.

Christ was speaking to the thief on his right. Both thieves
had been mocking Jesus. One had had a change of heart. The
younger one. He had rebuked his friend. He had confessed his
sins, and had begged a favor. "Lord, remember me when you
come into your kingdom." Lucifer heard Jesus promise: "Amen,
I say to you, this day you will be with me in paradise."

A murderer and a thief was going to paradise. A further
humiliation to the helpless lord of the pit! He had counted on
taking both these rogues to hell. Now one was already a saint!
He would be the first human creature to enter heaven! He would
lead all the other saints that were to be! And there would be
many saints, Lucifer knew. Many. Too many.

Hatred rose anew in him though he was still powerless, still groveling at the foot of the new Monarch of the world, the dying King of Sinners. Jesus would die. But only temporarily! He would raise himself from the dead through his own power. Lucifer swore to himself that he would do all he could to prevent it. But he knew that Jesus would beat him again. The King was dying? He would live forever.

But how long would he reign? And over how large a kingdom?

Lucifer would live forever too, he reasoned; and his malice would give him strength to fight, even when he felt most helpless. He began to strengthen himself by making sure of the thief on the left. This man was a petty crook, a cheap killer. He was no prize for the mighty angel of evil; but the Christ had bled for him as well as for the thief on the right. To snatch the fellow down to hell would be a petty triumph, but a triumph. Lucifer needed triumphs, however petty. Too bad he couldn't have nailed John and James, the sons of Zebedee, to those outside crosses — and have made them die in despair. Their mother had wanted to see them enthroned on each side of Jesus. Would she have watched them die as calmly as the virgin mother watched her Son? It was an idle thought — but it led to thoughts not so idle. Some day he would kill not only John and James, but all the other Apostles. He had only to wait, and watch, and keep on hating.

Christ Jesus was speaking again. His voice was still a whisper, but there was power in it and affection. "Woman, behold your son. Son, behold your mother."

He had given his loved ones all he had. His counsel, his wisdom, his example, his love, his suffering, his very body and blood. Now he was giving them his most precious possession, his mother. She would be not only John's mother. She would be the mother of all the children of God, the living and the dead and the generations not yet born.

Lucifer felt this as a new outrage. The woman he so hated, the woman terrible as an army, would strive to keep her children from him. If he could only do something about that! But he could not move. He would not be able to move until Jesus died. He must lie here, chanting with all the other angels, the wicked and the blessed, "Holy, holy, holy, Lord God of Hosts!" Truly this was hell!

Jesus spoke again, with anguish.

"My God, my God, why have you forsaken me?"

Was he trying to recite David's psalm that began with those words? Lucifer, who liked to boast, especially to the high priests, of his knowledge of Scripture, quoted parts of the psalm — testing it for an answer to his question. "I am a worm and no man; the reproach of men and the outcast of the people. All that saw me laughed me to scorn; they have spoken with the lips and wagged the head. 'He hoped in the Lord, let him deliver him; let him save him, seeing he delighted in him.' "

All afternoon, in this crazy darkness, in this rioting, protesting, rebelling earth; men had cried reproaches. They had indeed laughed him to scorn. True, some had run away in fear and trembling when the ground moved under them, and the heavens moaned, and the last star withdrew its light. But many still remained, waiting for him to work some miracle, or to die.

"He saved others," one said. "He cannot save himself." "He is a man like other men," a second shouted. "He suffers like other men. He bleeds like other men. He will die like other men. He was a good teacher, a great organizer, a splendid preacher, an inspired storyteller. But of course he was not, is not, God." . . . "Show us a sign, miracle worker," a third cried. "If you be the Christ, let's see you come down from your cross."

Was Jesus answering them with David's psalm?

Lucifer remembered other verses: "My strength is dried up like a potsherd, and my tongue has cleaved to my jaws; and you have brought me down into the dust of death. . . . Many dogs have encompassed me; the council of the wicked have besieged me. They have dug my hands and my feet. They have numbered all my bones. . . . They parted my garments among them, and upon my vesture they cast lots. . . .

"The poor shall eat and be filled; and they that seek the Lord will praise him; their hearts will live forever and forever . . . and all the kin of the Gentiles shall adore him. The kingdom is the Lord's and he shall have dominion over all the nations. . . . To him my soul shall live; and my seed shall serve him. There shall be declared to the Lord a generation to come; and the heavens shall show forth his justice to a people that shall be born, which the Lord has made!"

Was Jesus merely reciting that psalm or did he actually feel God had forsaken him? Had his divinity decreased so much that he was, for the moment, unaware of it? Had his humanity so increased that his Godhead was not felt? Nobody knew better than Lucifer that the absence of God is hell. Could it be that Jesus wanted to suffer not only in his body, but also in his soul?

Jesus spoke again. Loudly this time, and without any feeling of desolation in his tones.

Fever raged in him, searing him, and he said: "I thirst."

Immediately one of the soldiers picked up a sponge, soused it in vinegar, put it on the end of his spear, and placed it against Jesus' mouth. Jesus would not drink it.

Lucifer felt somewhat encouraged. Through all eternity, he reflected, fools would offer vinegar to God — especially when he thirsted for the fine vintage of their love. What an ally hell had in human nature! Lucifer could rely on it. Perhaps he could even strengthen it with his own spirit. Why not?

If Jesus could give his body and blood, with his soul and divinity; why couldn't Lucifer give his devilish spirit to his friends?

CHAPTER XXXIII

For three hours Mary stood in front of the cross, sometimes looking up at Jesus, sometimes looking beyond him to the lights burning in the city he loved. Caiphas had given instructions that Jesus should not see the holy city as he died. He intended to show that Jerusalem had turned its back on Jesus. He didn't understand that he had caused Jesus to turn his back on the city.

"Jerusalem, Jerusalem," Mary mourned, remembering her Son's lament, "thou that killest the prophets and stonest them that are sent against thee, how often would he have gathered together thy children, as the hen gathers her chickens under her wings! But thou wouldst not; thou wouldst not."

The lanterns and torches made weird lights and shadows on the cross, and on the Man who clung to it. Sometimes the Man seemed to be in flight, his arms taking on the semblance of wings. Sometimes he seemed to be a lover stretching out his arms wide to embrace the world. He was dying, but he was still making love to all men, even those who hated and despised him.

Mary was thinking with her heart — and thinking eased, a little, the agony made by the swords.

"A river rose in Eden, watering the garden. It separated into four branches. There are three here, flowing out of this new Eden. Three red rivers. One flows from his right hand. One flows from his left. One flows from his two feet, nailed together so tightly they seem but one.

"Three rivers, watering the gardens of the world, irrigating arid lands, letting deserts bloom, making the poorest soils fruitful! Three rivers singing God's music as they hurry on their errands. Three rivers bringing beauty and holiness to all God's children.

"I see three rivers springing from the body of God. They carry cargoes of grace, freight rich enough to redeem every slave that Satan has in his keeping. There should be four rivers in this Eden. Where is the fourth?"

Jesus spoke to her, his voice much stronger than it had been. "It is consummated!"

Yes, Mary agreed. It was done. He had finished his Father's business. It was time he should go home. She waited patiently for the sword of his farewell.

She remembered how it was during those three days when he was lost to her and Joseph. How would it be now? How could she live without him? She did not know. But it was his will to die. She willed it too. It was his will that she should live without him. She made it her will.

And then she heard him cry out, with a tremendous joy, "Father, into your hands I commend my spirit!"

Joy! Joy and triumph. He had gone into his Father's arms. Would he mind if she wept for him, as he had wept before the tomb of Lazarus, his dear friend?

Gradually the light of heaven returned, and the darkness disappeared. And great rocks split in various parts of the world, Mary learned — days later. And earthquakes shattered buildings in Jerusalem and other cities, shook the great gold Temple, and tore the veil of the Holy of Holies from top to bottom.

Caiphas had rent his garments in fury when Jesus proclaimed

himself the very Son of God. Had God rent the veil to show his fury to the high priests and their friends?

Graves opened and spat out their dead. People all over the Hill of the Skull, and throughout Jerusalem, beat their breasts in sorrow and in fear, knowing what they had done. The centurion gaped at the body of the middle cross, and said, "Truly, he was the Son of God!"

Men came to examine the bodies. They saw the thieves were still alive. They would be defiled if the robbers were not taken down before the Sabbath came. They must be dead when they were taken down. They must be quickly killed. Jesus was already dead. They were not concerned with him. They broke the legs of the thieves and watched them die. The centurion seized a lance, and with it opened Jesus' heart, so that blood and water poured out of it.

"Four rivers," Mary said in her heart. "Four rivers flowing out of Eden, bearing the greatest treasure of almighty God. Four rivers that will bring even the weariest sailors back to the paradise they seek. Rivers of God's most precious blood! May they flood the world with mercy and with love!"

John stood with her. Mary Magdalen was near, still weeping, So was the other Mary. Salome was on her knees, sobbing like a child. People came. People went. Men brought kind strangers to her. They tried to comfort her. But what could anyone do for so deep a wound as hers?

The sun was shining again. The dust was thick. The wild flowers had been trampled by many feet, and here and there lay pieces of bread and fish and cheese. Some had been picnicking here while Jesus suffered.

Mary met Joseph of Arimathea. She met Nicodemus. They were among the masters of Israel; but they believed in Jesus. They volunteered to take the body from the cross. John helped.

John was her new son. She had always loved him, even as Jesus had. He would be a great saint. All the Apostles would be great saints — all that were still alive.

They placed him, finally, in her arms, that she might hold him for a little while. They had washed his hands and his face and his feet. They had put a clean new robe on him. She held him tightly.

She rocked him a little. What else could a mother do? She had rocked so many, many babies in her life! For a few moments, she had the sweet illusion that he was a child again. She was at home, in Nazareth. She was rocking him to sleep. And Joseph was singing a lullaby in his soft sweet voice.

> The night was clear. The winds were cold.
> The Baby cried.
> Hush, Baby, hush!
> Baby, don't cry.
> We'll make a quilt so warm for you
> Out of the little things we do.
> Baby, don't cry.

The illusion faded. Reality plunged another sharp blade into her heart. The Baby had grown up. The Baby had died upon a cross. The Baby must be laid in a tomb. Right now. Before the Sabbath broke.

They had spices and oils. They had linen cloths. They worked swiftly, deftly, lovingly, not bothering to wipe their eyes. Why couldn't she cry as they did — wholeheartedly, thoroughly, without restraint?

They laid him in the tomb — a small cave carved out of a limestone rock. It was like the cave in which he was born, but much smaller, much cleaner, much nicer. They said good-bye to him and left him there. They rolled a great wheel of stone against the door of the tomb, to block it. She could still hear the frightful grinding noise it made against the limestone tomb. That noise, she feared, would grate on her ears forever.

She walked away blindly, John at her side. She walked straight to the middle cross, and rested there, and wept, and tried to smile at John. But she couldn't see him.

"Don't weep any more," John begged her. "Think of it as the triumph it is."

"Yes," she said. "A triumph. It takes great faith to see that though. He is dead and in his tomb. His Apostles are scattered, his followers gone, his enemies in control of his kingdom. His teachings will be forgotten, and his blood and his tears will be of no avail to many. But perhaps he wanted it that way — so that our faith might grow."

"The good thief on the cross had faith," John said. "And he had hope too. And love."

"And by an act of love," Mary said, "he erased a life of crime."

She leaned against the cross. It gave way a trifle. She eased it back to its upright position. It moved away from her. She rocked it, mechanically, like a cradle.

Illusion came back to her. Again the Baby was in her arms, and a lullaby was in Joseph's mouth, and the world was filled with peace.

"Blessed are they that mourn, Jesus said, for they shall be comforted."

It was Joseph's voice she heard. It stirred her as of old.

"Yet why do you mourn, my sister, my spouse? Remember what he said of the sign of Jonas, that on the third day he would rise.

"It was on the third day we found him in the Temple. On the third day he will find you. He will wipe away all tears. He will find Peter and Mary Magdalen, those tremendous penitents, and all the others. He will comfort them and you. He will walk with you and dine with you. He will ascend to his Father; but not until he has prepared his sheep for the coming of the Holy Ghost.

"Rejoice, my dove, my perfect one, my Mary. You have made beautiful and most holy the seven swords God thrust into your heart. He will use them, with your tears, and with the tears and the blood and the suffering and the death of your Son — your Son and his. Many will be sanctified through them.

"Rejoice and smile now through your tears, and show the Lord your love.

"Beautiful are your feet among the flowers, O Prince's daughter; and lovelier than all the blossoms in the fields, and sweeter in their fragrance than rare spices or the costliest incense, for they have walked always in the footsteps of the Lord.

"Thou art beautiful, my love — mother, wife, and maiden all in one. Thou art sweet and comely as Jerusalem.

"Put me as a seal upon thy heart, as a seal upon thy arm, for love is strong as death. Nay, love is stronger than death. Love is eternal. Love is stronger than life. Love is stronger than hell and earth allied in battle against high heaven.

"Love is as strong as a cross, this cross you rock like a cradle."

Mary turned radiant eyes on John — eyes wet with tears yet shining with the love of God and man.

"The cross is a cradle for love," she told him. "Even a child can find peace there, hard as it is, if his mother rocks him, and he listens for his Father's voice. Take me home now, son. It is the Sabbath. It is the feast of the Passover, the feast of the Lamb of God. The Lamb has been sacrificed, and all the world is invited to the feast."